# ExplOring maths

Class Book

**Anita Straker, Tony Fisher, Rosalyn Hyde, Sue Jennings and Jonathan Longstaffe**

**1**

Published and distributed by Pearson Education Limited, Edinburgh Gate, Harlow, Essex, CM20 2JE, England
www.longman.co.uk

First published 2009
ISBN-13 978-1-405-84404-8

**Freelance development editor: Sue Glover**

Typeset by Tech-Set, Gateshead

Printed and bound in Great Britain at Scotprint, Haddington

The publisher's policy is to use paper manufactured from sustainable forests.

**Picture credits**

The publisher would like to thank the following for their kind permission to reproduce their photographs:

(Key: b-bottom; c-centre; l-left; r-right; t-top)

**www.dreamstime.com:** 43; **Alamy Images:** Ace Stock Ltd 141c; Bubbles Photolibrary 26; Colin Underhill 38b; David Crausby 101r; Design Pics 130; Gabe Palmer 41, 61; Gemstone Images 252; Ian Shaw 241; Jeff Morgan Education 250tl; Leander 82l; mediacolor's 247b; Neil Overy 161t; Paul Rapson 255; Photo Alto 332r; Profimedia International s.r.o. 75; Robert Fried 128; Stefan Sollfors 203 (a); Steven May 90; Stockbyte 208r; tompiodesign.com 256; Tony Cordoza 124; Trevor Smith 97b; **alveyandtowers. com:** 129b; **Art Directors and TRIP photo Library:** 161b, 269; **Bananastock:** 22l (inside frame); **Bridgeman Art Library Ltd:** 87, 113; Alice in Wonderland by Mendoza, Philip (1898-1973) Private Collection/ © Look and Learn 172; **Bureau International Des Poid et Mesures, Paris:** 139t; **Corbis:** David Madison 137; James Emmerson / Robert Harding World Imagery 205l; Jim Craigmyle 42t; Mark Karrass 14; Roy Morsch / zefa 298; **DK Images:** 135, 140b, 181, 184, 205r, 276; Andy Crawford 227, 332; Dave King 23b; Gary Ombler, courtesy John Rigg, The Robot Hut 78; Steve Gorton 226l, 226r; Ian O'Leary 208b; Mike Dunning 73r; Paul Bricknell 133br, 138, 138l, 334l, 334r; Paul Goff 253; Sarah Ashun 329r, 330; Tim Knox 101l; Tim Ridley 12; **Getty Images:** David Woodfall 58t; Stockbyte 249; Stu Forster 198b, 286b; **iStockphoto:** 22 (frame), 57r, 103, 133t, 133bl, 203tl, 203 (b), 206tl, 220tl, 250r, 280l; An Yunak 203 (c); Andrew Kendall 24; Anna Bryukhanova 39r; Anneke Schram 104; Bart Sadowski 263; Cheng Ping- Hung 73l; Chris Schmidt 141r; Christine Glade 35r; Darren Hendley 198t; Denise Torres 203 (d); Dietmar Klement 203 (e); Eileen Hart 84; Gabor Izso 83b; Gary Alvis 123b; Gene Krebs 32; Geno Sajko 16; Graeme Purdy 203 (f); Hugo Chang 197; Imre Cikajlo 280r; Jakub Semeniuk 206bl; Jennifer Sheets 286t; Jonathan Maddock 160t; Jostein Hauge 315; Keith Johnson 200; Kelly Cline 297; Kelviin Wakefield 312; Kriss Russell 251; Les Cunliffe 187; Lisa F Young 60, 250bl; Lisa Thornberg 97t; Liv Friis-Larsen 139b; Long Ha 40; Maria Bibikova 63; Mark Evans 199; Martin Bowker 162; Matej Michelizza 109; Murat Koc 332c; Owen Price 67l; Pali Rao 46, 191; Paul Tessier 67r; Pierrette Guertin 123r; Radu Radzan 140t; Rafal Zdeb 23tr; Richard Gunion 203tr; Sandra O'Claire 27; Sean Locke 101c, 168; Simon Krzic 110; Simon Podgorsek 220r; Stefan Klein 61b; Stephan Hoerold 39l; Steven Allan 83t; Sue McDonald 22r (inside frame); Viktor Kitaykin 23tl; Xavi Arnau 70r; Yusuf Anil Akduygu 70l; **Jupiter Unlimited:** 23tc, 141l, 206tr, 206br, 212; Brand X Pictures 220tc; **No Trace:** 301; **Pearson Education Ltd:** 3, 6, 31, 35l, 38t, 47l, 47br, 47bl, 50, 51, 54 (1), 54 (3), 54 (6), 54 (10), 54 (15), 55, 57l, 129t, 150l, 150c, 150r, 152t, 152cl, 152c, 152cr, 211r, 244, 296r, 296l; Anita Straker 2, 28, 53, 64, 76, 88, 91, 96, 119, 127, 315; David Mager 37, 91l, 213tc, 213tr; Frank LaBua 247t; John Paul Endress 213tl; Karen Mancinelli 213b; Richard Embery 61t; Russ Lappa 58b; Scott Foresman 94; **PunchStock:** Moodboard 284; Uppercut 254; Valueline 278; **Rex Features:** Alan Lewis 211; E. M. Welch 160b; **Science Photo Library Ltd:** 57c

**Cover images:** *Front:* **Alamy Images:** Kavita Favelle

All other images © Pearson Education

**Picture Research by:** Kevin Brown

**Acknowledgements**

We are grateful to the following for permission to reproduce copyright material:

International Olympic Committee for data about "Where Summer & Winter Olympic Games have been held since 1964" and "gold, silver and bronze medals won by Ian Thorpe" published on www.olympic.org/uk/, reproduced with permission; and The Wikipedia Foundation for the "Image compass" image.

Every effort has been made to trace the copyright holders and we apologise in advance for any unintentional omissions. We would be pleased to insert the appropriate acknowledgement in any subsequent edition of this publication.

# Contents

# Properties of numbers

**This unit will help you to:**

- spot multiples of 2, 5 and 10;
- spot odd and even numbers;
- add or subtract a multiple of 10.

## 1 Multiples of 10

This lesson will help you to add or subtract a multiple of 10.

### Exercise 1

**Multiples of 10** end in zero.

Multiples of 10 are coloured pink.

To add or subtract a multiple of 10, count on or back in tens.

The units digit stays the same.

### Example

Work out 38 + 40.

Start at 38. Count on 4 tens.
48, 58, 68, 78.

**Answer: 78**

| 1 | 2 | 3 | 4 | 5 | 6 | 7 | 8 | 9 | 10 |
|---|---|---|---|---|---|---|---|---|---|
| 11 | 12 | 13 | 14 | 15 | 16 | 17 | 18 | 19 | 20 |
| 21 | 22 | 23 | 24 | 25 | 26 | 27 | 28 | 29 | 30 |
| 31 | 32 | 33 | 34 | 35 | 36 | 37 | 38 | 39 | 40 |
| 41 | 42 | 43 | 44 | 45 | 46 | 47 | 48 | 49 | 50 |
| 51 | 52 | 53 | 54 | 55 | 56 | 57 | 58 | 59 | 60 |
| 61 | 62 | 63 | 64 | 65 | 66 | 67 | 68 | 69 | 70 |
| 71 | 72 | 73 | 74 | 75 | 76 | 77 | 78 | 79 | 80 |
| 81 | 82 | 83 | 84 | 85 | 86 | 87 | 88 | 89 | 90 |
| 91 | 92 | 93 | 94 | 95 | 96 | 97 | 98 | 99 | 100 |

(1) Work these out.

a $40 + 50$     b $120 + 40$     c $290 + 70$     d $360 + 50$

e $36 + 40$     f $134 + 20$     g $472 + 50$     h $287 + 30$

(2) Work these out.

a $90 - 50$     b $130 - 40$     c $280 - 60$     d $420 - 50$

e $153 - 40$     f $261 - 50$     g $413 - 30$     h $915 - 80$

**3** The rule is 'add 10' or 'subtract 10'.
Copy and complete these.

a ...     10     20     ...     ...     ...     ...     70

b 320     ...     ...     ...     ...     ...     ...     250

c ...     ...     450     ...     430     ...     ...     ...

d ...     ...     ...     620     ...     ...     650     ...

**4** Work these out.

a $421 + 500$       b $176 + 800$       c $935 - 300$       d $652 - 400$

**5** Play **Tens** with a partner.
You need a dice.

Each player draws this strip.

### Rules

- Take turns.
- Roll the dice. Each spot is worth 10.
- Write your score in a box on your strip.
- Carry on until both strips are full.
- Now roll again.
- If your score is on your grid, cross it out.
  If not, wait for your next turn.
- The winner is the first to cross out all their numbers.

**6** Copy the triangle.

Use all these numbers.

20    30    40    50    60

Write one number in each circle.

Each side of the triangle must add up to 100.

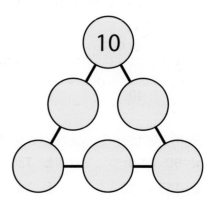

**7**　**a** What is the 3rd multiple of 10?　　　**b** What is the 7th multiple of 10?

　　**c** What is the 10th multiple of 10?　　**d** What is the 15th multiple of 10?

　　**e** What is the 50th multiple of 10? Explain how you worked it out.

**8**　Copy this.

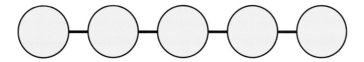

Use all these numbers.

　　　10　　20　　30　　40　　50

Write one number in each circle.
The difference between joined numbers must be more than 10.

**Points to remember**

- **Multiples of 10** end in 0.
- To add or subtract a multiple of 10, count on or back in tens. The units digit stays the same.
- **Consecutive numbers** follow in order, e.g. 4, 5, 6, 7, …

## 2 Multiples of 2 or 5

This lesson will help you to spot multiples of 2 or 5.

### Exercise 2

**Consecutive numbers** follow in order, e.g.

**3, 4, 5, 6**

Here are some consecutive **multiples of 5**.
They all end in 0 or 5.

**5, 10, 15, 20, 25, …**

Here are some consecutive **multiples of 2**.
They all end in 0, 2, 4, 6 or 8.

**2, 4, 6, 8, 10, …**

**1** Which are multiples of 5?

435    28    52    865    220    94

**2** Which are multiples of 2?

47    23    870    146    118    95

**3** Copy and complete these.

  **a** 1    3    ...    ...    ...    11    ...    ...

  **b** ...    4    6    ...    10    ...    ...    ...

  **c** 15    20    ...    ...    ...    ...    45    ...

  **d** 60    ...    50    ...    40    ...    ...    ...

**4** Work these out.

  **a** $40 + 25$      **b** $53 + 35$      **c** $32 + 55$      **d** $90 + 15$

**5** Here are the prices of 5 cakes.

5p        10p        15p        20p        25p

3 different cakes fit in a box.

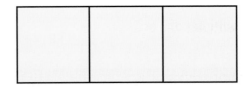

  **a** A box of 3 cakes costs 55p. What is the cost of each cake?

  **b** A box of 3 cakes costs 60p. What is the cost of each cake?

  **c** A box of 3 cakes costs 35p. What is the cost of each cake?

**6** This sum uses 2s and 5s.

$$5 + 5 + 5 + 2 + 2 + 2 = 21$$

Make sums with 2s and 5s. Make all the numbers from 6 to 20.

**7** Use a set of digit cards from 1 to 9.

Put them in 3 piles.
The numbers in each pile must add up to a multiple of 5.

**Extension problem**

**8** 　**a** What is the 3rd multiple of 5?　　**b** What is the 5th multiple of 5?

　**c** What is the 10th multiple of 5?　　**d** What is the 15th multiple of 5?
Explain how you worked it out.

## Points to remember

- **Multiples of 5** end in 5 or 0.
- **Multiples of 2** end in 0, 2, 4, 6 or 8.
- **Even numbers** are 0, 2, 4, 6, 8, 10, … They all end in 0, 2, 4, 6 or 8.
- **Odd numbers** are 1, 3, 5, 7, 9, 11, … They all end in 1, 3, 5, 7 or 9.

## 3 Odd and even numbers

This lesson will help you to work with odd and even numbers.

**Exercise 3**

The **even numbers** are 0, 2, 4, 6, 8, 10, 12, 14, …
They all end in 0, 2, 4, 6 or 8.

The **odd numbers** are 1, 3, 5, 7, 9, 11, 13, 15, …
They all end in 1, 3, 5, 7 or 9.

① Which are even?

27     428     550     63     225     354

② Which are odd?

431     253     90     42     108     425

③ Copy and complete these.

a  494     496     498     …     …     …

b  605     603     601     …     …     …

c  …     …     233     235     237     …     …

④ Play **Odds and evens** with a partner.
You need two sets of cards from 1 to 10.

Shuffle the cards. Spread them face down.

**Rules**

◉ One of you is 'Even'. The other is 'Odd'.

◉ Each of you turns over one card.

◉ If the total is odd, then 'Odd' wins the two cards.

◉ If the total is even, then 'Even' wins the two cards.

◉ Carry on until all the cards are won.

◉ The player with the most pairs wins.

9 + 8 = 17
17 is **odd** so 'Odd'
wins this pair.

⑤ Write three odd numbers with a sum of 11.

⑥ Write three even numbers with a sum of 20.

⑦ Peter buys a burger.
It costs between 50p and £1.

He pays for it using an odd number of 20p coins.

How much does the burger cost?

**8** You need a set of cards from 1 to 9.

| 1 | 2 | 3 | 4 | 5 | 6 | 7 | 8 | 9 |

Arrange the cards like this.

The numbers in each row, column and diagonal must add up to an odd number.

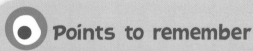

## Extension problem

**9**  
 **a** What is the 5th even number?   **b** What is the 10th even number?

**c** What is the 15th even number?   **d** What is the 20th even number?

**e** What is the 50th even number?
Explain how you worked it out.

### ⊙ Points to remember
- odd − odd = even
- even − even = even
- odd − even = odd
- even − odd = odd

# How well are you doing?

## Properties of numbers (no calculator)

**1** Which are multiples of 10?

20    46    301    580    400    95

**2** *2006 Progress Test level 3*

The first odd number is 1.
What is the sixth odd number?

**3** *2001 level 3*

Look at these cards.

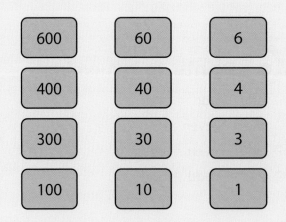

a   Which two cards add together to give a total of 70?

Now choose two different cards that add together to give a total of 70.

b   Three of the cards add together to give a total of 70.

Which three cards are they?

c   The difference between the numbers on two of the cards is 70.

Which two cards are they?

4 *2003 level 3*

Look at these cards.

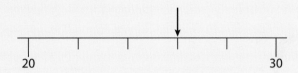

What is the biggest even number you can make with these cards?

5 Look at this number line.

```
        ↓
 |----|----|----|----|----|
20                      30
```

What value does the arrow show?

6 Which are odd numbers?

26     132     49     87     228     503

7 Write the next three numbers.

263     273     283     293     …     …     …

# Properties of shapes

**This unit will help you to:**

- ⊙ name, visualise, describe, draw and make 2D and 3D shapes;
- ⊙ identify right angles;
- ⊙ identify horizontal and vertical lines;
- ⊙ describe the position of a square on a grid.

## 1 2D shapes

This lesson will help you to name, visualise, describe and draw 2D shapes.

### Exercise 1

A **polygon** is a 2D shape with straight sides.

A shape with three straight sides is a **triangle**.

A shape with four straight sides is a **quadrilateral**.

A **rectangle** and a **square** are special types of quadrilateral.

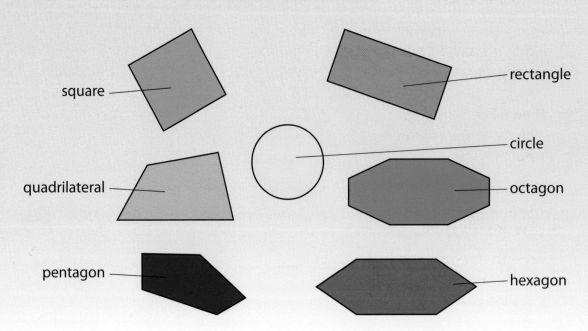

You will need square dotty paper, a pencil and a ruler.

① Here are some partly finished polygons.

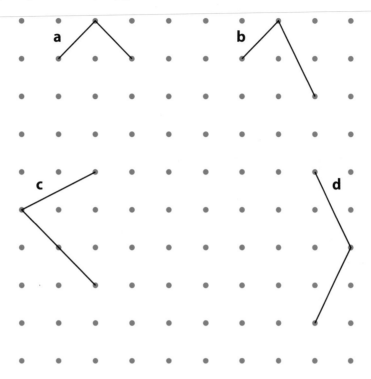

Copy the diagrams. Complete them to make:

  **a**  a triangle        **b**  a quadrilateral      **c**  a pentagon      **d**  a hexagon

②  **a**  Draw a line 4 cm long.
     This is the shortest side of a triangle.
     Draw the triangle.

    **b**  Draw another line 4 cm long.
     This is the longest side of a triangle.
     Draw the triangle.

③  **a**  Draw a line 3 cm long.
     This is one side of an octagon.
     Draw the octagon.

    **b**  Draw another line 3 cm long.
     This is one side of a hexagon.
     Draw the hexagon.

    **c**  Draw another line 3 cm long.
     This is one side of a pentagon.
     Draw the pentagon.

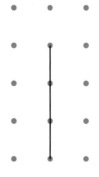

**4** **a** Draw a square on your dotty paper.

   **b** Draw a four-sided polygon that is not a square.

   **c** Explain why this shape is not a square.

   **d** Draw two more four-sided polygons that are not squares.
   Write their names next to them.

> ## ● Points to remember
>
> ⊙ A **polygon** is a 2D shape with straight sides.
>
> ⊙ A shape with
>    - **3** sides is a **triangle**;
>    - **4** sides is a **quadrilateral**;
>    - **5** sides is a **pentagon**;
>    - **6** sides is a **hexagon**;
>    - **7** sides is a **heptagon**;
>    - **8** sides is an **octagon**.

## 2 **3D shapes**

This lesson will help you to name, visualise, describe and make 3D shapes.

## Exercise 2

This picture shows some 3D shapes.

cylinder

cone

cube

pyramid

sphere

triangular
prism

cuboid

You will need a **set of 3D shapes** and some **interlocking cubes**.

(1) Look at the 3D shapes on page 12.

Copy the table. For each 3D shape, write the number of faces of each type.

| Solids | Number of faces | | | |
|---|---|---|---|---|
| | squares | rectangles | circles | triangles |
| cube | | | | |
| cylinder | | | | |
| square-based pyramid | | | | |
| cuboid | | | | |
| triangular prism | | | | |

(2) Write the names of two different shapes that have:

a  at least one square face;

b  at least one curved face;

c  at least one triangular face.

(3) Use 12 interlocking centimetre cubes each time.

a  Make a cuboid. Write its length, width and height.

b  Make a different cuboid. Write its length, width and height.

c  Make a different cuboid. Write its length, width and height.

(4) How many interlocking centimetre cubes do you need to make:

a  a cube with side 3 cm?

b  a cuboid with length 5 cm, width 2 cm and height 6 cm?

⊙ **Points to remember**

⊙ **2D shapes** are flat. They have sides and vertices.
The sides can be straight or curved.

⊙ **3D shapes** are *solids*. They have faces, edges and vertices.
The faces can be flat or curved.
The edges can be straight or curved.

# 3 Angles and lines

This lesson will help you to identify right angles and horizontal and vertical lines.

## Exercise 3

The angle turned by the minute hand of Big Ben in one hour is a **full turn**.

The angle turned by the minute hand of Big Ben in 15 minutes is a **quarter turn**.

A quarter turn is called a **right angle**.

A right angle is often marked on diagrams with a small square.

**Horizontal lines** run in the same direction as the horizon.

**Vertical lines** are upright. They go straight up and down.

Horizontal and vertical lines are at right angles to each other.

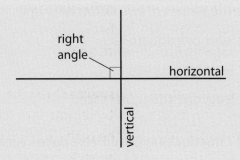

You will need your folded right angle, a set square and **G1.1 Resource sheet 3.1**.

①   Is the angle between the hands a right angle?
Write Yes or No.

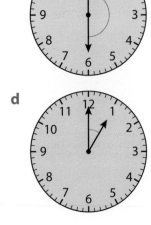
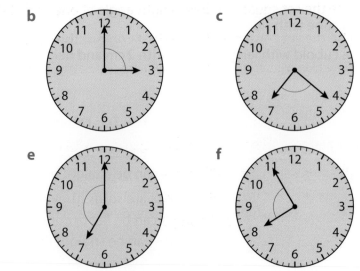

② Write the name of each shape and the number of right angles in it.

**a** 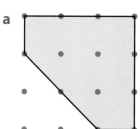  **b** 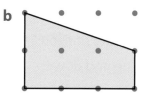  **c**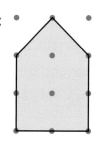

**d**  **e** 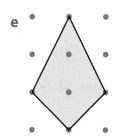  **f**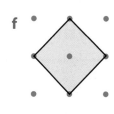

③ Look at diagram 1 on **Resource sheet 3.1**.
Find all the right angles in the shapes.
Use your right angle to check.
Mark each right angle with an R.

④ Look at diagram 2 on **Resource sheet 3.1**.
It shows the route taken by remote control cars.
Find the right angles in the paths.
Mark each right angle with an R.

⑤ Use your set square to draw a route for a remote control car.
Label the right angles.

⑥ **a** Draw a line 5 cm long.
Use the set square to draw a right angle at one end of the line.

**b** Use the set square to draw a right angle at the other end of the 5 cm line.

**c** Join the ends of the new lines. Write the name of the shape you have made.

## Extension problem

⑦ Use squared dotty paper to draw polygons with:

**a** five sides and one right angle;

**b** four sides and four right angles;

**c** four sides and one right angle;

**d** five right angles.

## Points to remember

⊙ A **right angle** is a quarter of a whole turn.

⊙ **Horizontal lines** run in the same direction as the horizon.

⊙ **Vertical lines** are upright. They go straight up and down.

⊙ Horizontal and vertical lines are at right angles to each other.

## 4 Identifying positions

This lesson will help you to describe and find the position of squares on a grid of squares.

### Did you know that...?

The game **Battleships** has been played since the 1930s.

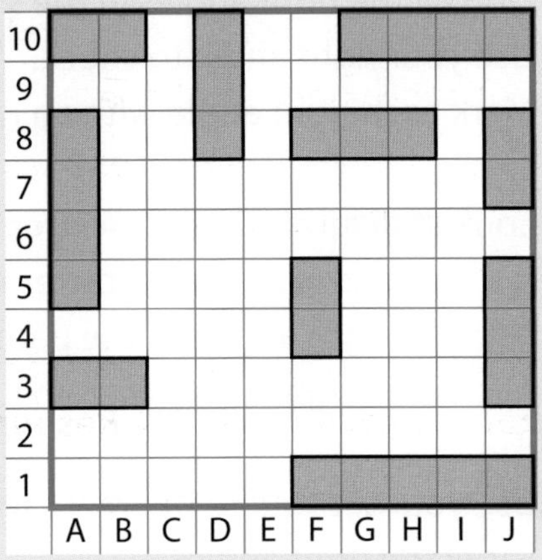

The game might have been invented by prisoners.

They used to shout out the coordinates to prisoners in other cells.

## Exercise 4

To describe the position of a square on the grid, you say the column letter and the row number like this: B3.

Always go across (horizontally) and then up (vertically).

In the diagram:

⊙ the orange cross is at position C3,

⊙ the blue circle at E4 and

⊙ the green triangle at B1.

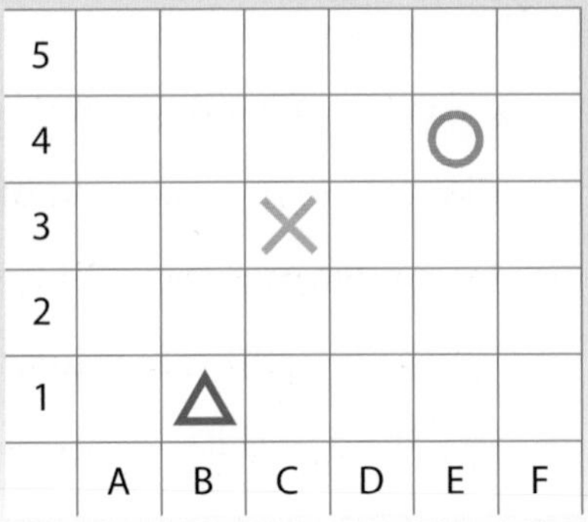

You will need squared paper, a ruler and some coloured pencils.

**1** Write the position of:

    **a** the purple square

    **b** the green square

    **c** the pink square

    **d** the orange square

    **e** the yellow square.

**2** **a** Copy this grid.
    Colour these squares:
    C2, B5, C5, D4, C4, B4, C3, D5

    **b** What shape have you made?

    **c** Make a new copy of the grid.
    Shade your own shape.
    Write the position of each square
    in your shape.

**3** Play **Battleships** with a partner.
You will each need **G1.1 Resource sheet 4.1** and a coloured pencil.

On your upper grid shade:

- 1 aircraft carrier (5 squares)

- 1 battleship (4 squares)

- 1 submarine (3 squares)

- 1 tug (2 squares)

Ships can be horizontal or vertical but not diagonal.

## Rules

- Player 1 says the position of a square where one of Player 2's ships might be.

- Player 2 says if it is a hit or a miss.

- On their lower grid, Player 1 colours the square red for a hit and blue for a miss.

- It is now the other player's turn.

- The winner is the first to find all the other player's ships.

**Extension problem**

 **4**   Molly places a counter on square D4.

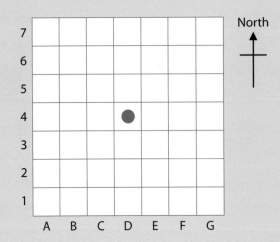

**a**   Molly moves the counter 2 squares west and 3 squares north.
Write the position of the square she lands on.

**b**   Molly places the counter on square B3.
She moves if 5 squares east and 3 squares north.
Write the position of the square she lands on.

**c**   Molly places the counter on square D6.
She moves it 4 squares south and 1 square east.
Write the position of the square she lands on.

## Points to remember

⊙ To give the position of a square on a grid, write the letter for the column
and the number for the row.

# How well are you doing?

## Can you:

- name, visualise, describe and make 2D and 3D shapes?
- identify right angles?
- describe the position of a square on a grid?

1   *2005 level 3*

Look at the diagrams showing 3D shapes.

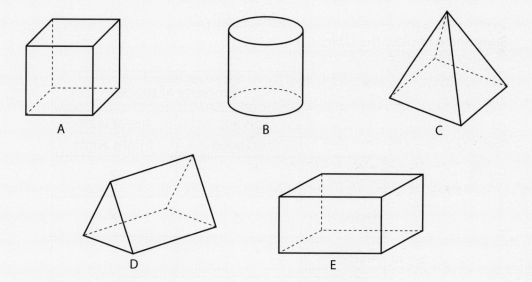

a   One of the shapes has one square face and four triangular faces.
Write the letter of this shape.

b   Two of the shapes have six faces.
Write the letters of these shapes.

c   Now look at this diagram showing another 3D shape.

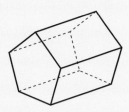

How many faces does the shape have?

Here are four shapes on a square grid.

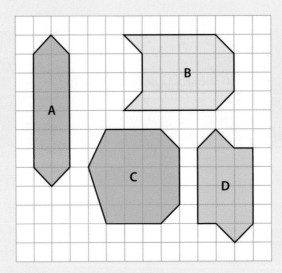

Copy and complete the table.

| | Property of shape | |
|---|---|---|
| | is an octagon | has at least 1 right angle |
| shape A | ✗ | ✓ |
| shape B | ✓ | ✗ |
| shape C | | |
| shape D | | ✓ |

**3** *2004 level 3*

Here are some right-angled triangular tiles.
The tiles are all the same shape and size.

Two of these tiles join to make a triangle.

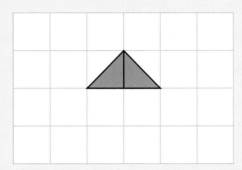

Use squared paper.

**a** Show how eight of these tiles join to make a square.

**b** Show how four of these tiles join to make a square.

**4** *2005 level 3*

Which square is exactly halfway between squares A1 and G7?

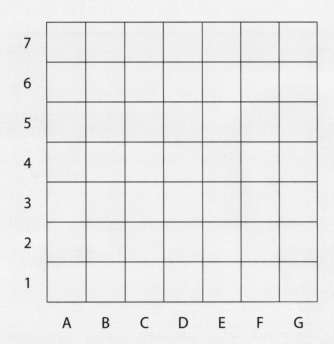

# Functional skills 1

## Displaying photos

**This group activity will help you to:**

- work out how to solve a practical problem;
- choose the maths to do to solve it;
- present your solution.

You will need a ruler, scissors, three pieces of thin card and sticky tape.

Work with a partner.

## General information

You can buy picture frames to show several photos.

A cut out mask hides part of the photos.

Two rectangles have been cut out in the green mask to show these photos.

Joe has three photos. Each photo measures 15 cm by 10 cm.

Two are wide and one is tall.

Joe sticks them on A4 card
to go in a photo frame.

He may overlap them.

He takes another piece of card
to be a mask.

He plans and measures carefully
where the holes will go.

He cuts out the holes and
sticks the mask on top of his photos.

Then he puts his photos in the frame.

## Problem

### Mounting photos

Design and make a mask for some photos.

Start by cutting out three 10 cm by 8 cm 'photos' from one piece of card.
Roughly draw the pictures.

Stick the photos on a second piece of card.

Then make your mask. Measure carefully where the holes will go.

Cut out the holes and stick the mask in position.

Be ready to join another pair to evaluate your work.

# Adding and subtracting

**This unit will help you to:**

- ◉ read, write, order and round numbers;
- ◉ remember number facts to 20;
- ◉ add and subtract in your head and on paper;
- ◉ use a calculator;
- ◉ solve problems.

## 1 Place value, ordering and rounding

This lesson will help you to read, write, round and order numbers.

### Did you know that...?

The Romans wrote numbers using letters.

| I | is 1 |
| V | is 5 |
| X | is 10 |
| L | is 50 |
| C | is 100 |
| VII | means 5 + 1 + 1 = **7** |
| CLVI | means 100 + 50 + 5 + 1 = **156** |

### Exercise 1

328 = 300 + 20 + 8

| Hundreds | Tens | Units |
|----------|------|-------|
| 3 | 2 | 8 |

three hundred and twenty-eight

507 = 500 + 7

| Hundreds | Tens | Units |
|----------|------|-------|
| 5 | 0 | 7 |

five hundred and seven

## Example

Write in order: 246, 72, 405. Start with the smallest.

The smallest number is **72**. It has only **7** tens and **2** units.
246 has **2** hundreds. It is the next smallest.
405 has **4** hundreds. It is the biggest.

The order is 72, 246, 405.

**(1)** Write in figures.

   **a** five hundred and twenty-four       **b** ninety-six

   **c** four hundred and seven           **d** three hundred and thirty

   **e** eight hundred and seventeen      **f** one hundred and ten

**(2)** Write in words.

   **a** 405          **b** 50          **c** 321          **d** 620

**(3)** What numbers are **a**, **b**, **c**, **d** and **e**?

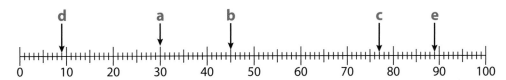

**(4)**  **a** Make the smallest possible number.

   **b** Make the biggest possible number.

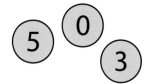

**(5)** Write in order. Start with the smallest.

   **a** 63    33    66    36         **b** 206    602    262    620

   **c** 818    118    188    181      **d** 533    353    535    553

**(6)** Round to the nearest 100.

   **a** 660        **b** 320        **c** 750        **d** 699

**(7)** Round to the nearest 10.

   **a** 35         **b** 544        **c** 308        **d** 277

(8) Play **Make the smallest** with a partner.
You need two packs of cards from 0 to 5.

**Rules**

- ⊙ Put the cards face down. Shuffle them.

- ⊙ Pick three cards each.

- ⊙ Make the smallest possible number with your three cards.
  For example, with **0**, **3** and **2** you could make **230**.

- ⊙ The player with the smallest number wins a point.

- ⊙ Put the cards back face down. Shuffle and pick again.

- ⊙ The winner is the first to get 10 points.

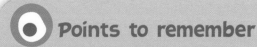
## Points to remember

- ⊙ To order numbers, look at the digits.
- ⊙ < means 'less than' and > means 'more than'.
- ⊙ Round up fives, e.g. 425 rounds to 430.

## 2 Number facts to 20

This lesson will help you to remember number facts to 20.

### Exercise 2

To do sums in your head you must know
**number facts to 20**.

This is useful when you work out change from 20p.

It helps if you know fact families, such as:

$$6 + 5 = 11 \qquad 11 - 5 = 6$$

$$5 + 6 = 11 \qquad 11 - 6 = 5$$

Do questions 1 to 4 in your head as quickly as you can.

**1**
  **a** $9 + \square = 11$
  **b** $6 + \square = 14$
  **c** $7 + \square = 12$
  **d** $4 + \square = 9$
  **e** $7 + \square = 15$
  **f** $9 + \square = 17$

**2**
  **a** $\square + 8 = 13$
  **b** $\square + 9 = 12$
  **c** $\square + 6 = 11$
  **d** $\square + 7 = 16$
  **e** $\square + 8 = 11$
  **f** $\square + 9 = 15$

**3**
  **a** $7 + \square = 11$
  **b** $\square + 6 = 12$
  **c** $9 + \square = 16$
  **d** $\square + 4 = 12$
  **e** $4 + \square = 13$
  **f** $\square + 8 = 14$

**4**
  **a** $15 - \square = 4$
  **b** $\square - 13 = 6$
  **c** $12 - \square = 7$
  **d** $\square - 3 = 12$
  **e** $17 - \square = 2$
  **f** $\square - 14 = 6$

**5** Each letter of PARTY has a value.

P A R T Y
1 2 3 4 5

Add up the numbers in the words below in your head.

  **a** AT
  **b** TAP
  **c** RAT
  **d** YAP
  **e** ART
  **f** RAY
  **g** TRY
  **h** RAP
  **i** TRAY

**6** Choose two different numbers from this set.

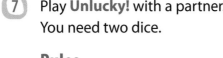

Find their sum.
You can get ten different answers.
Write each sum and its answer.

**7** Play **Unlucky!** with a partner.
You need two dice.

### Rules

- Each player should draw five boxes.

  Write a different number from 3 to 13 in each box.

- Take turns. Roll the dice. Add the numbers.

- Work out how many more you need to make 15.

- If the other player has that number, you may cross it out in their boxes. If not, wait for your next turn.

- The winner is the first to cross out all the other player's numbers.

## Extension problem

**8** You need one dice.

Draw four boxes like this.   ☐ + ☐ − ☐ = ☐

- Roll the dice. Write the score in the first box.

- Roll again. Write the score in the last box.

- Write numbers in the other two boxes to make a correct sum.

- Write the sum in your book.

Roll again to make more sums in the same way.

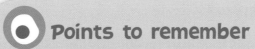
# 3 Mental strategies

This lesson will help you to add and subtract in your head.

## Exercise 3

An **empty number line** can help you do sums in your head.

### Example

Work out 35 + 7.

First count on from 35 to 40.

This uses 5 from the 7.

There is 2 more to count on.

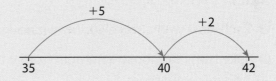

$$35 + 7 = 35 + 5 + 2$$
$$= 40 + 2$$
$$= 42$$

1. Do these in your head as quickly as you can. Write the answer.

   **a** 17 + 3      **b** 27 + 3      **c** 37 + 3      **d** 47 + 3

   **e** 16 + 5      **f** 26 + 5      **g** 36 + 5      **h** 46 + 5

   **i** 14 + 9      **j** 24 + 9      **k** 34 + 9      **l** 44 + 9

   **m** 18 + 7      **n** 28 + 7      **o** 38 + 7      **p** 48 + 7

(2) Here is a number line from 0 to 100.

0  10  20  30  40  50  60  70  80  90  100

Do these in your head. Use the number line to help. Write the answer.

**a** 60 + 20      **b** 55 + 15      **c** 70 + 25

**d** 90 − 70      **e** 65 − 45      **f** 80 − 35

(3) In this grid, each number is the sum of the row number and the column number.

For example, 48 is 46 + 2.

59 is 58 + 1.

| + | 2 | 1 | 3 |
|---|---|---|---|
| 46 | 48 | 47 | 49 |
| 58 | 60 | 59 | 61 |

Copy and complete this grid.

| + | 6 | 10 | 8 |
|---|---|---|---|
| 35 | ... | ... | ... |
| 69 | ... | ... | ... |

(4) Play **Target 100** with a partner.

### Rules

- Each start with a score 50. Write it down.

- Take turns to choose a number from 4 to 9.
  Add it to your score.
  Write down the new score.

- The first to reach exactly 100 wins.

### Extension problem

(5) Do these in your head as quickly as you can.

**a** 28 + 3      **b** 49 + 6      **c** 35 + 9      **d** 47 + 4

**e** 16 + 7      **f** 86 + 5      **g** 24 + 8      **h** 37 + 6

**i** 52 + 9      **j** 28 + 9      **k** 78 + 5      **l** 56 + 8

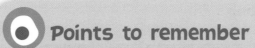

**Points to remember**

⊙ You can add numbers in any order.

⊙ To add in your head:
   – start with the biggest number.
   – bridge through a multiple of 10.

⊙ Draw a number line to explain your method.

## 4 More mental strategies

This lesson will help you to get better at adding and subtracting in your head.

### Exercise 4

You can work out pairs of numbers that make 100 in your head.
This is useful when you are working out change from £1, for example.

**Example**

Toby buys an ice cream cone for 54p.

Work out his change from £1.

In your head, count up to the next ten.

   $54 + 6 = 60$

Now count on to 100.

   $60 + 40 = 100$

So the change is $6 + 40 = 46p$.

① Do in your head as quickly as you can. Write the answer.

| | | | |
|---|---|---|---|
| **a** $12 - 3$ | **b** $22 - 3$ | **c** $32 - 3$ | **d** $42 - 3$ |
| **e** $16 - 8$ | **f** $26 - 8$ | **g** $36 - 8$ | **h** $46 - 8$ |
| **i** $13 - 9$ | **j** $23 - 9$ | **k** $33 - 9$ | **l** $43 - 9$ |
| **m** $15 - 7$ | **n** $25 - 7$ | **o** $35 - 7$ | **p** $45 - 7$ |

**2** Maria went to the Farm Shop.

| Item | Price |
|---|---|
| tomatoes | 69p |
| carrots | 34p |
| apples | 50p |
| potatoes | 72p |
| cabbage | 67p |
| pepper | 28p |
| courgettes | 46p |
| eggs | 72p |
| milk | 36p |
| apple juice | 85p |

Find her change from £1 for:

**a** apples

**b** apple juice

**c** a cabbage

**d** carrots

**e** courgettes

**f** eggs

**g** milk

**h** a pepper

**i** potatoes

**j** tomatoes

**3** Draw this. Do the puzzle.

**Across**
1 Add 7 to 98
3 90 minus 9
5 Subtract 8 from 51
7 94 plus 6

**Down**
1 9 more than 95
2 5 less than 63
4 The sum of 94 and 6
6 Take 4 from 35

4 Play **Target zero** with a partner.

**Rules**

- Start with a score 50. Write it down.

- Take turns.

- Choose a number from 4 to 9.
  Subtract it from your score.
  Write down the new score.

- The first to reach exactly zero wins.

Play several times.

5 Do these in your head as quickly as you can.

a  58 − 9    b  46 + 7    c  31 − 6    d  25 + 8

e  42 − 7    f  37 + 4    g  93 + 7    h  54 − 8

i  66 + 6    j  54 − 5    k  78 + 3    l  36 − 8

6 Use only these numbers. You can repeat a number if you want to.

| 1 | 2 | 5 | 7 | 8 |

Make different subtractions like this. Write them down.

☐☐ − ☐ = ☐

How many correct subtractions can you make?

Now try making sums like this.

☐☐ + ☐ = ☐☐

**7** Write the answer.

a 128 + 6    b 514 + 7    c 345 + 8    d 427 + 9

e 423 − 8    f 252 − 7    g 439 + 9    h 521 − 6

 **Points to remember**

⊙ To take away, bridge through a multiple of 10.

⊙ Draw a number line to explain your method.

# 5 Addition

This lesson will help you to use a written method to add numbers.

## Exercise 5

To find a **sum** or a **total**, add up all the numbers.

You can **add** numbers in columns.

Line up the units under the units, the tens under the tens, and so on.

### Example

Calculate 259 + 437.

Estimate the answer: 300 + 400 = 700

```
      259
  +   437
      ───
       16   add the ones            It may be quicker like this.
       80   add the tens                           259
      600   add the hundreds                   +   437
      ───                                          ───
      696   find the total                         696
                                                    1
```

**1** Estimate the answer.

a 88 + 43    b 22 + 57    c 69 + 17

d 45 + 39    e 98 + 32    f 53 + 71

g 421 + 386    h 784 + 58    i 123 + 67

(2) Work these out. Show your working.

a   76 + 67

b   146 + 80

c   540 + 260

d   437 + 513

e   276 + 655

f   424 + 381

(3) Jenny has £54 of savings.
She saves another £38.
How much savings does she have now?

(4) A sandwich costs 75p.
A glass of milk costs 48p.
An apple costs 34p.

How much does it cost to buy:

a   a glass of milk and an apple?

b   a sandwich and a glass of milk?

c   a sandwich, a glass of milk and an apple?

(5) 278 adults and 63 children watch a film at the cinema.
How many people altogether are watching the film?

(6) There are 168 jelly beans in a jar.
How many jelly beans are there in two jars?

(7) In a week:   Lauren eats 27 jelly beans;
Jamal eats 36 jelly beans;
Ivan eats 19 jelly beans.

What is the total number of jelly beans they eat in a week?

(8) Sarah buys a sofa for £462.
She buys a carpet for £370.
She buys a lamp for £56.

How much does Sarah spend altogether?

## Extension problem

(9) Work these out. Show your working.

a   4832 + 3176

b   581 + 2935

c   4692 + 5437

## Points to remember when you add

- Look first at the numbers.
- Do it in your head if you can.
- Estimate the answer so you can check it.
- To add in columns, line up the digits.
  Put units under units, tens under tens, …

## 6 Subtraction

This lesson will help you to use a written method to subtract numbers.

### Exercise 6

To find a **difference**, take the small number from the big number.

You can subtract by writing numbers in columns.

Line up the units under units, tens under the tens, and so on.

### Example

Calculate 624 − 157.

Use rounding to estimate the answer.
Estimate: 600 − 200 = 400

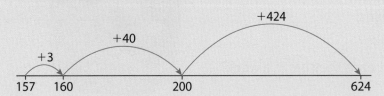

$$\begin{array}{r} 624 \\ -\ 157 \\ \hline 3 \text{ to make } 160 \\ 40 \text{ to make } 200 \\ 424 \text{ to make } 624 \\ \hline 467 \end{array}$$

1. Estimate the answer.

   a  41 − 32          b  98 − 47          c  79 − 57

   d  81 − 28          e  103 − 66         f  119 − 92

   g  517 − 86         h  463 − 274        i  125 − 38

2. Work these out. Show your working.

   a  162 − 90         b  410 − 85         c  920 − 280

   d  317 − 84         e  726 − 358        f  935 − 271

(3) Alison has £350. She buys a TV for £162.
How much does she have left?

(4) There are 318 people at a concert.
124 of them are children.
How many are adults?

(5) Amy needs £425 to fly to Greece.
She has saved £368 towards it.
How much more does she need to save?

(6) Darren's bike cost £216.
Amelia's bike cost £178.

    **a** How much change did Darren get from £300?

    **b** How much less did Amelia pay for her bike
    than Darren?

(7) Darren did a 126 mile bike ride.
He got a flat tyre after 78 miles.
How much further did he ride?

## Extension problems

**8** Work these out. Show your working.

    **a** 2756 − 1235         **b** 4803 − 1467         **c** 9126 − 849

**9** Anna buys a new car for £8255.
She gets £4370 for her old car.
How much more does she have to pay?

## ◉ Points to remember when you subtract

- ⊙ Look first at the numbers.
- ⊙ Do it in your head if you can.
- ⊙ Estimate the answer so you can check it.
- ⊙ To subtract in columns, line up the digits.
  Put units under units, tens under tens, …
- ⊙ Count up from the smaller number.

# 7 Word problems

This lesson will help you to solve word problems.

## Exercise 7

A **word problem** tells a story about numbers.

You have to work out what calculation to do and the best way to do it.

### Example

One cup cake weighs 278 grams.
Another cup cake weighs 315 grams.
What is the total weight of the cup cakes?

You need to work out 278 + 315.

Estimate the answer.
Round each number to the nearest 100.

300 + 300 = 600

Calculate 278 + 315.

The answer 593 is close to the estimate of 600.

The answer is 593 grams.

$$\begin{array}{r} 278 \\ +315 \\ \hline 593 \end{array}$$

1. 39 girls and 45 boys take part in a fun run.
   How many children take part in the fun run?

2. Ella has £103 in her bank account.
   She takes out £38.
   How much does Ella have left?

3. Max drives 283 miles to Manchester.
   He stops for a coffee after 137 miles.
   How much further does he have to drive?

4. Dan collects 236 cans for recycling.
   Zoe collects 128 cans.

   a  How many cans do they collect in total?

   b  How many more cans does Dan collect than Zoe?

(5) A small bar of soap costs 78p.
A big bar of soap costs 93p.
How much do they cost altogether?

(6) The small bar of soap weighs 168 grams.
The big bar of soap weighs 214 grams.
How much lighter is the small bar of soap?

(7) 182 adults and 374 children went to a museum.

a How many people went to the museum?

b What is the difference between the number of adults and number of children who visited the museum?

(8) Tom and Jack have tickets for the Skate Park.
Tom has 48 tickets.
Jack has 36 tickets.

a How many more tickets has Tom than Jack?

b How many tickets have Tom and Jack altogether?

(9) A shop in New York is selling three jigsaws for 8 dollars.

The jigsaws have 500, 120 and 375 pieces.

What is the total number of pieces in the three jigsaws?

## Extension problem

(10) a The sum of three numbers is 425.
Two of the numbers are 124 and 138.
Work out the other number.

b Two numbers have a difference of 200.
The small number is 85.
What is the big number?

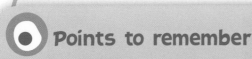

## Points to remember

⊙ Read the problem carefully.

⊙ Write down the sum you will do.

⊙ Decide on your method.

⊙ Do the sum. Show your working.

⊙ Check your answer makes sense.

⊙ Include units in your answer.

## 8 Calculator skills

This lesson will help you to use a calculator.

### Exercise 8

A calculator is useful for solving problems.
You need to decide what calculations to do.

### Example

Rose paid £139 for a tennis racquet.
She paid £38 for some tennis balls.
She paid £128 for some tennis lessons.
How much did Rose pay altogether?

Work out 139 + 38 + 128.

Press these calculator keys: ①③⑨＋③⑧＋①②⑧＝

The display shows      305.

So Rose paid £305 altogether.

**Use your calculator.**

① You can get 20 in the display using just five keys.
Here are two ways.

①⑤＋⑤＝ 20      ②③－③＝ 20

Find four more ways to do it.

| 3 | 16 | 9 | 22 | 15 |
|---|----|---|----|----|
| 20 | 8 | 21 | | 2 |
| 7 | 25 | 13 | 1 | 19 |
| 24 | 12 | 5 | 18 | 6 |
| 11 | 4 | 17 | 10 | 23 |

**②** This is a **magic square**.
The numbers in each row, each column and each diagonal add up to the same magic number.

   **a** What is the magic number?

   **b** One of the numbers is missing.
      What should it be?

**③** Use your digit cards 1 to 5.

Arrange them to make a sum like this.

What is the smallest answer you can get?

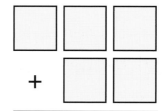

**④** Play **Going down** with a partner.
You need a calculator between you.

**Rules**

○ Put 100 in the display.

○ The first player subtracts a number from 1 to 9,
says the answer, then presses ⌐=⌐ to check.

○ The second player subtracts a number from 1 to 9,
says the answer, then presses ⌐=⌐ to check.

○ Carry on taking turns.

○ The winner is the player to get to exactly 50.

**⑤** Make 554 in your calculator display.

```
554.
```

Use only these keys.

② ⑥ ⑧ – =

**6** Make your calculator display show 100.

Use only these keys.

Record how to do it.

### Extension problem

**7** Make all the numbers 1 to 12 using only these keys.

$4 \; + \; - \; \times \; \div \; =$

You can use each key as often as you like each time.

## ⦿ Points to remember when you use a calculator

- ⊙ Estimate the answer so you can check it.
- ⊙ When you enter a calculation, press $=$ after the last number.
- ⊙ If you make a mistake, clear the display and start again.

## 9 Number investigations

This lesson will help you to investigate number problems.

### ⓘ Did you know that...?

**Sic bo** is a game from Asia.
It is played with three dice.
You can score from 3 to 18.
The score on these three dice is 15.

### Exercise 9

**1** You can play **Sic bo** with two dice.
With two dice, how can you score each of the numbers 2 to 12?

(2) Dave supports his local football club.

The club badge costs 50p.

Dave has lots of 20p, 10p and 5p coins.
In how many different ways can he pay for the badge?

Draw a table like this to help you.

| Number of 20p coins | | | | | | | | | | | |
|---|---|---|---|---|---|---|---|---|---|---|---|
| Number of 10p coins | | | | | | | | | | | |
| Number of 5p coins | | | | | | | | | | | |

(3) Kate wants to send a present to her friend.

She has lots of 4p, 5p and 10p stamps.

She must put 30p more in stamps on her parcel.

How can she do it?

Write all the possibilities.

(4) Pick three of these numbers.
They can be the same or different.
The three numbers must total 20.

There are 10 different ways to do it.
Make a list of them all.

## Extension problem

 **5** Choose a two-digit number.
The tens digit must be bigger than the units digit.
Reverse the digits.
Subtract.
Reverse the result.
Add.

Repeat for other two-digit numbers.
What do you notice?

Now try some three-digit numbers.
What happens?

**Example**

$$\begin{array}{r} 72 \\ -\ 27 \\ \hline 45 \\ +\ 54 \\ \hline 99 \end{array}$$

## Points to remember

- ⊙ Read problems carefully.
- ⊙ Work systematically.
- ⊙ Look for patterns.
- ⊙ See if there is more than one answer.

# How well are you doing?

## Can you:

- read, write, order and round numbers?
- add and subtract in your head and on paper?
- use a calculator?
- solve problems?

## Addition and subtraction (no calculator)

**1** *2002 Mental Test level 3*

What number is the arrow pointing to on the number line?

300            400

**2** *2006 Progress Test level 3*

The total of these bank notes is 35 euros.

What is the total amount of these bank notes?

a

b

**3** *2005 Progress Test level 3*

Copy and complete these calculations.

a  46 + ☐ = 73                    b  55 − ☐ = 29

**4** *2003 Progress Test level 3*

Work out the answers to these calculations.

a  257 + 649                    b  541 − 382

## Addition and subtraction (calculator allowed)

**5** *2006 Progress Test level 3*

The first five odd numbers add up to 25.
What do the first six odd numbers add up to?

**6** *1996 KS2 level 3*

Tim buys a 19p postcard.
He pays exactly 19p with five coins.

What could the five coins be?

**7** *2000 level 3*

Add 238 to 567, then subtract 143.

**8** *2002 level 3*

Colin and Jenny are playing a game.

a  Colin has four hundred and thirty points.
   Write this number in figures.

b  Jenny has six hundred and nine points.
   Write this number in figures.

c  Jenny is playing a game.
   She has six hundred and nine points.
   The winner is the first to get one thousand points.
   How many more points does Jenny need to win the game?

# Patterns and sequences

**This unit will help you to:**

- spot multiples of 2, 3, 4, 5 and 10;
- spot and use number patterns;
- continue sequences;
- multiply numbers.

 **Did you know that...?**

You often see patterns made from **shapes**.

These tiling patterns are in a bakery in Mexico.

You can also get patterns made from **numbers**.

## 1 Multiplication patterns

This lesson will help you to understand multiplication and remember tables for 2, 5 and 10.

### Exercise 1

$3 + 3 + 3 + 3 = 12$
$3 \times 4 = 12$

$4 + 4 + 4 = 12$
$4 \times 3 = 12$

① I have these coins.
How much altogether do I have?

| |  10 | 5 | 2 |
|---|---|---|---|
| a | 3 | 4 | 6 |
| b | 1 | 7 | 8 |
| c | 6 | 6 | 4 |
| d | 2 | 8 | 9 |
| e | 4 | 9 | 7 |

② Play **Fives and tens** with a partner.
You need **two** packs of digit cards from **0 to 8**.

0 1 2 3 4 5 6 7 8

Shuffle the cards.
Put the pack face down.

## Rules

◉ The first player draws one grid. The other player draws the other grid.

| 5 | 35 | 10 |
|---|---|---|
| 50 | 30 | 80 |

| 15 | 70 | 25 |
|---|---|---|
| 40 | 20 | 60 |

◉ Take turns.

◉ Turn over the top card.

◉ Choose whether to multiply by 5 or by 10.

◉ If the answer is on your grid, cross it out.

◉ The winner is the first player to cross out all their numbers.

**3** Write the answers.

a $6 \times 2$    b $3 \times 5$    c $10 \times 7$    d $2 \times 8$    e $7 \times 3$

f $9 \times 10$   g $5 \times 5$    h $3 \times 8$    i $9 \times 2$    j $9 \times 3$

**4** You can write $5 + 5 + 5$ as $5 \times 3 = 3 \times 5$.

Write as a multiplication:

a $4 + 4 + 4$        b $2 + 2 + 2 + 2 + 2$        c $6 + 6 + 6 + 6$

d $12 + 12$          e $15 + 15 + 15$            f $21 + 21 + 21 + 21$

**5** Copy and complete these.

a Put 2 or 10 in each box.

$$26 = \boxed{\phantom{0}} + \boxed{\phantom{0}} + \boxed{\phantom{0}} + \boxed{\phantom{0}} + \boxed{\phantom{0}}$$

b Put 5 or 10 in each box.

$$30 = \boxed{\phantom{0}} + \boxed{\phantom{0}} + \boxed{\phantom{0}} + \boxed{\phantom{0}} + \boxed{\phantom{0}}$$

c Put 2 or 5 in each box.

$$16 = \boxed{\phantom{0}} + \boxed{\phantom{0}} + \boxed{\phantom{0}} + \boxed{\phantom{0}} + \boxed{\phantom{0}}$$

**Extension problem**

**6** Ella has only 10p, 5p and 2p coins.

She pays for a comic costing 73p using exactly 14 of her coins.

Which coins did she use?

 **Points to remember**

⊙ 3 groups of 5 is $5 + 5 + 5 = 15$, or $5 \times 3 = 15$

⊙ $3 \times 5 = 5 \times 3$

⊙ Answers in the 5 times table are **multiples of 5**.

⊙ The 4th multiple of 5 is $5 \times 4 = 4 \times 5 = 20$.

⊙ Learn by heart tables for 2, 5 and 10.

# 2 Simple sequences

This lesson will help you to find and use the rule for a sequence.

## Exercise 2

A **sequence** of numbers follows a **rule**.

3    4    5    6    7    8    9    10    11

### Example

Here is a sequence. The rule is 'add 3'.

$$4, \quad 7, \quad 10, \quad 13, \quad 16, \quad \ldots$$

Write the next three numbers.

**4,    7,    10,    13,    16,    19,    22,    25**

---

1. Write the next three numbers.

   a  1,    6,    11,    16,    …,    …,    …

   b  101,    91,    81,    71,    …,    …,    …

   c  3,    7,    11,    15,    …,    …,    …

   d  2,    5,    8,    11,    …,    …,    …

   e  64,    60,    56,    52,    …,    …,    …

2. Write the rule. Then write the next three numbers.

   a  1,    4,    7,    10,    …,    …,    …

   b  22,    32,    42,    52,    …,    …,    …

   c  50,    43,    36,    29,    …,    …,    …

   d  99,    93,    87,    81,    75,    69,    …,    …,    …

   e  2,    11,    20,    29,    …,    …,    …

**3** Draw the next pattern for each of these sequences.

a

b

**4** Look at this sequence of beads.
The beads are numbered.

| 1 | 2 | 3 | 4 | 5 | 6 | 7 | 8 | 9 |

The sequence continues in the same way.

a  What are the numbers of the first three yellow beads?

b  What are the numbers of the next three yellow beads?

c  What are the numbers of the first three red beads?

d  What are the numbers of the next three red beads?

e  What are the numbers of the first three blue beads?

f  What are the numbers of the next three blue beads?

g  What colour is the 11th bead?

h  What colour is the 15th bead?

**Extension problem**

**5** Here is a repeating pattern of shapes.

Each shape is numbered.

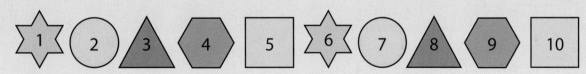

The pattern continues in the same way.

Write the numbers of the next two **stars** in the pattern.

# 3 More multiplication patterns

This lesson will help you to learn the 3 and 4 times tables.

## Exercise 3

**Multiples of 3** divide exactly by **3**.

Numbers in the **3 times table** are multiples of 3.

| 0 | 1 | 2 | 3 | 4 |
|---|---|---|---|---|
| 5 | 6 | 7 | 8 | 9 |
| 10 | 11 | 12 | 13 | 14 |
| 15 | 16 | 17 | 18 | 19 |
| 20 | 21 | 22 | 23 | 24 |
| 25 | 26 | 27 | 28 | 29 |
| 30 | 31 | 32 | 33 | 34 |
| 35 | 36 | 37 | 38 | 39 |

| 0 | 1 | 2 | 3 | 4 |
|---|---|---|---|---|
| 5 | 6 | 7 | 8 | 9 |
| 10 | 11 | 12 | 13 | 14 |
| 15 | 16 | 17 | 18 | 19 |
| 20 | 21 | 22 | 23 | 24 |
| 25 | 26 | 27 | 28 | 29 |
| 30 | 31 | 32 | 33 | 34 |
| 35 | 36 | 37 | 38 | 39 |

**Multiples of 4** divide exactly by 4.

Numbers in the **4 times table** are multiples of 4.

(1) Write the answers.

a  $9 \times 2$      b  $4 \times 5$      c  $3 \times 7$      d  $5 \times 8$      e  $8 \times 3$

f  $7 \times 5$      g  $4 \times 6$      h  $3 \times 10$     i  $2 \times 8$      j  $9 \times 4$

k  $3 \times 6$      l  $7 \times 4$      m  $9 \times 3$      n  $4 \times 8$      o  $4 \times 0$

(2) These numbers are the multiples of 3 from 3 to 30.
Two of them are missing. Which two are they?

21    9    15    3    30    24    6    12

**3** Look at this grid.

The number at the top of the column is multiplied by the number at the left of the row.

For example, $2 \times 3 = 6$.

| × | 2 | 8 |
|---|---|---|
| 3 | 6 | 24 |
| 2 | 4 | 16 |

Copy and complete this grid.

| × | 2 | 3 | 10 |
|---|---|---|---|
| 4 | | | |
| 5 | | | |
| 2 | | | |

**4** Use two of these numbers each time.

Copy and complete these.

**a** ...... × ...... = 12     **b** ...... × ...... = 20     **c** ...... × ...... = 24

**d** ...... × ...... = 30     **e** ...... × ...... = 15     **f** ...... × ...... = 40

**g** ...... × ...... = 32     **h** ...... × ...... = 18

**5** Play **Threes** with a partner.
You need two dice. Each spot is worth **3**.

**Rules**

○ Each player draws a 2 by 3 grid.

○ Take turns to roll the dice.

○ Write your score in a box.

○ Carry on until all the boxes are full.

○ Now take turns to roll the dice again.

○ If your score is on your grid, cross it out. If not, wait for your next turn.

○ The winner is the first to cross out all their numbers.

If you play again, make each spot worth **4**.

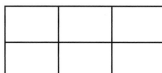

**6** Copy and complete these.

a Put 2 or 3 in each box. $12 = \square + \square + \square + \square + \square$

b Put 2 or 5 in each box. $13 = \square + \square + \square + \square + \square$

c Put 3 or 4 in each box. $17 = \square + \square + \square + \square + \square$

d Put 4 or 5 in each box. $22 = \square + \square + \square + \square + \square$

## ◉ Points to remember

⊙ **Multiples of 4** divide exactly by 4.

⊙ Numbers in the 4 times table are multiples of 4.

⊙ 12 is a multiple of 3 and a multiple of 4.
   It is in the 3 times table and the 4 times table.

⊙ Learn by heart tables for 3 and 4.

## 4 More sequences

This lesson will help you to use patterns to continue sequences.

### Exercise 4

You can make a sequence by using **patterns of shapes**.

1          3          6          10          15

**1** The numbers on these tickets form a sequence.

   **a** What is the rule for the sequence?

   **b** What numbers are on the next three tickets in the sequence?

   **c** Will 212 be in the sequence? Explain how you know.

**2** Here is a number chart.

Every third number has a circle on it.

The chart continues in the same way.

   **a** Here is another row in the chart.

| 26 | 27 | 28 | 29 | 30 |
|----|----|----|----|----|

     Which numbers should have circles on?

   **b** Will the number 300 have a circle on it?

     Write **Yes** or **No**. Explain how you know.

| 1 | 2 | ③ | 4 | 5 |
|----|----|----|----|----|
| ⑥ | 7 | 8 | ⑨ | 10 |
| 11 | ⑫ | 13 | 14 | ⑮ |
| 16 | 17 | ⑱ | 19 | 20 |
| ㉑ | 22 | | | |

**3** Here is a sequence made from dots and crosses.

  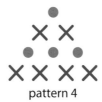

pattern 1    pattern 2    pattern 3    pattern 4

   **a** How many dots are there in pattern 5?

   **b** How many crosses are there in pattern 5?

   **c** How many dots are there in pattern 6?

   **d** How many crosses are there in pattern 6?

④ These patterns are made from squares and circles.

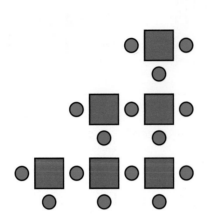

| Number of squares | Number of circles |
|-------------------|-------------------|
| 1 | 3 |
| 2 | 5 |
| 3 | 7 |

The sequence of patterns continues in the same way.

a How many circles are there in the pattern that has 4 squares?

b How many squares are there in the pattern that has 11 circles?

c How many squares are there in the 10th pattern?

d How many circles are there in the 10th pattern?

## Extension problems

⑤ The steps in this sequence are all the same. What are the two missing numbers?

1    …    …    13

⑥ Two numbers are missing in this sequence. What are they?

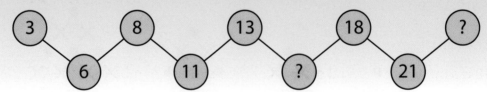

# 5 Using number patterns to solve problems

This lesson will help you to use number patterns to solve problems.

 **Did you know that...?**

Fibonacci

The step size in a sequence is not always the same.

The Italian **Fibonacci** found this sequence 800 years ago.
The rule is 'add the previous two numbers'.

$$0, \quad 1, \quad 1, \quad 2, \quad 3, \quad 5, \quad 8, \quad 13, \quad 21, \quad ...$$

The pattern is linked to the spirals you see in pineapples, fir cones and sunflowers.

## Exercise 5

Since $4 \times 6 = 24$, you know that 24 is a **multiple of 4** and a **multiple of 6**.

### Example

18 is a multiple of several different numbers. Which numbers are they?

Since $1 \times 18 = 18$, you know that 18 is multiple of 1 and a multiple of 18.

Since $2 \times 9 = 18$, you know that 18 is multiple of 2 and a multiple of 9.

Since $3 \times 6 = 18$, you know that 18 is multiple of 3 and a multiple of 6.

So 18 is a multiple of 1, 2, 3, 6, 9 and 18.

1. Write all the multiples of 3 from 3 to 30.

2. Write all the multiples of 4 from 4 to 40.

(3) 30 is a multiple of several different numbers.

Which numbers are they?
Write them all.

(4) The postman left 18 letters in Bridge Road.
Each house had some letters.

Some houses had 5 letters.
The rest had 2 letters each.

How many houses are there in Bridge Road?

(5) Tom has some goats and chickens.

He has 15 goats and chickens altogether.

They have 34 feet between them.

How many goats does Tom have?

How many chickens?

(6) Nasreen bought some 20p stamps and
some 10p stamps.
She spent £2 altogether.

She bought three times as many 10p stamps as 20p stamps.

How many 20p stamps did she buy?
How many 10p stamps?

(7) Ben has 37 CDs.
He puts all of them in piles.

Some piles have 4 CDs in them.
Some piles have 3 CDs in them.

How many piles of 3 CDs are there?
How many piles of 4 CDs?

## Extension problem

**8** Look at the numbers on this calendar.
Choose any square of four numbers. For example:

**Calendar**

Month __January__

| Sunday | Monday | Tuesday | Wednesday | Thursday | Friday | Saturday |
|--------|--------|---------|-----------|----------|--------|----------|
|        |        |         | 1         | 2        | 3      | 4        |
| 5      | 6      | 7       | 8         | 9        | 10     | 11       |
| 12     | 13     | 14      | 15        | 16       | 17     | 18       |
| 19     | 20     | 21      | 22        | 23       | 24     | 25       |
| 26     | 27     | 28      | 29        | 30       | 31     |          |

**a** The total of column 1 is 9 + 16 = 25
The total of column 2 is 10 + 17 = 27

What is the difference between the two totals?

Does this work for any square of four numbers?

**b** Find the total of each row of the 2 by 2 square.

What is the difference between the two totals?

Does this work for any square of four numbers?

**c** Add up the numbers in each diagonal of the 2 by 2 square.
What do you notice?

Does this work for any square of four numbers?

**d** What do you notice about the sequence of numbers in each column?

---

### Points to remember

- When you solve a problem, it may help to make a table.
- Work systematically.
- Work out the **step size** in a sequence. Use it to find the **rule**.

---

## 6 Multiplying by 10 or 100

This lesson will help you to multiply by 10 or 100.

### Exercise 6

When you **multiply** a number:

by **10**, its digits move **1 place to the left**;

by **100**, its digits move **2 places to the left**.

**Examples**

| | |
|---|---|
| 56 × 10 | 560 |
| 56 × 100 | 5600 |

Do questions 1 and 2 **without a calculator**.

1 Copy and complete these.

a  5 × 10 = …                    b  10 × 9 = …

c  6 × 100 = …                   d  100 × 7 = …

e  46 × 10 = …                   f  10 × 91 = …

g  30 × 10 = …                   h  10 × 30 = …

2 Copy and complete these.

a  3 × … = 30                    b  10 × … = 40

c  7 × … = 700                   d  100 × … = 500

e  39 × … = 390                  f  10 × … = 720

g  20 × … = 200                  h  10 × … = 800

3 **Use your calculator** to work these out.

a  3 × 10 × 10 = …      and      3 × 100 = …

b  9 × 10 × 10 = …      and      9 × 100 = …

c  1 × 10 × 10 = …      and      1 × 100 = …

d  Write what you noticed.

4 **Use your calculator** to work these out.

a  50 × 3 = …      and      5 × 3 × 10 = …

b  70 × 2 = …      and      7 × 2 × 10 = …

c  40 × 5 = …      and      4 × 5 × 10 = …

d  60 × 4 = …      and      6 × 4 × 10 = …

e  Write what you noticed.

Do questions 5 to 8 **without a calculator**.

5 Work these out.

a  30 × 5              b  90 × 2              c  50 × 7

d  70 × 3              e  60 × 5              f  80 × 4

**6** This recipe makes **1 box** of peanut biscuits.

## Peanut biscuits

| | |
|---|---|
| 95 g | flour |
| 50 g | sugar |
| 75 g | peanut butter |
| 20 g | peanuts |
| 1 | egg yolk |
| 5 ml | water |

Write the recipe to make **10 boxes** of peanut biscuits.

**7** Change:

a  3 cm to millimetres.

b  6 m to centimetres.

c  95 cm to millimetres.

d  £9 to pence.

e  50 mm to centimetres.

f  400p to pounds (£).

**8** Holly makes a fruit drink for 10 people. She uses:

3 bottles of water

75 ml of orange juice

30 slices of lemon

80 g of sugar

16 mint leaves

What does Holly need to make fruit drink for 100 people?

## ⦿ Points to remember

- ⦿ When you **multiply**:
  - × 10, the digits move left 1 place;
  - × 100, the digits move left 2 places.
- ⦿ × 100 is the same as × 10 then × 10.
- ⦿ To do 50 × 3, work out 5 × 3 then multiply by 10.
- ⦿ To change cm to mm, multiply by 10.
- ⦿ To change m to cm, multiply by 100.

# 7 Multiplying bigger numbers

This lesson will help you to multiply numbers, using a calculator when needed.

## Exercise 7

### Example

Calculate $37 \times 5$.

$37 = 30 + 7$

| × | 30 | 7 |
|---|----|---|
| **5** | 150 | 35 |

$150 + 35 = 185$

Split 37 into $30 + 7$.

Make a grid.

Multiply 30 by 5 to get 150.

Multiply 7 by 5 to get 35.

Find the sum of 150 and 35.

The answer is **185**.

Do questions 1 and 2 **without a calculator**.

1 Work these out.

    **a** $50 \times 3$      **b** $60 \times 4$      **c** $20 \times 5$      **d** $90 \times 2$

    **e** $70 \times 4$      **f** $80 \times 5$      **g** $30 \times 2$      **h** $40 \times 3$

2 Calculate these.

    **a** $18 \times 5$      **b** $29 \times 4$      **c** $38 \times 5$

    **d** $56 \times 2$      **e** $64 \times 3$      **f** $46 \times 4$

**3** This is the menu of the corner café.

### Menu

| | |
|---|---|
| burger | 94p |
| egg | 38p |
| chips | 42p |
| sausage | 68p |
| cola | 57p |
| water | 28p |

**a** Lewis buys four colas for him and three friends.
What does it cost him?

**b** Rupa buys egg, chips and cola.
How much does she pay?

**c** Sam buys two sausages and two portions of chips.
What does he pay altogether?

**d** Jade buys three bottles of water.
How much change does she get from £1?

**4** **Use your calculator**.

The table shows the cost of a one-week holiday in Spain.

| June | |
|---|---|
| Week beginning | Cost |
| 1 June | £298 |
| 8 June | £219 |
| 17 June | £234 |
| 22 June | £259 |
| 29 June | £289 |

**a** Five friends go to Spain for one week on 8 June.
What does it cost them altogether?

**b** The week beginning 29 June costs more than
the week beginning 22 June.
How much more?

**c** Mrs Green and her son go to Spain for a week.
They leave on 1 June.
What does it cost for both of them?

**5** Play **Make the most** with a partner.
You need a dice and a calculator.

Each player should draw three boxes like this.

### Rules

- One of you rolls the dice.

- Each of you secretly writes the score in one of your boxes. You can't change it later.

- Do this two more times.

- Now work out the answers to your calculations **without the calculator**.

- **Use the calculator** to check the answers.

- The player with the biggest answer scores a point.

- The winner is the first to get 5 points.

If you play again, the player with the smallest answer scores a point.

### Extension problem

 **6** Work these out **without a calculator**.

a  153 × 4          b  231 × 5          c  432 × 3

---

## Points to remember

- Use a grid for TU × U, and a calculator for bigger numbers.
- Read problems carefully. Write down the sum you will do.
- Do the sum. Use a calculator if you may.
- If you do a pencil-and-paper sum, show your working.
- Check your answer is about the right size.
- Record your answer. Include units.

# How well are you doing?

**Can you:**

- spot multiples of 2, 3, 4, 5 and 10?
- spot and use number patterns?
- continue sequences?
- multiply numbers?

## Patterns and sequences (no calculator)

**1** *2004 Progress Test level 3*

a Copy these number chains. Write the missing numbers.

**Rule:** Add 3 each time.

1 4 7 10 … …

**Rule:** Multiply by 2 each time.

1 2 4 8 … …

b Here is a different number chain.

20 16 12 8 4 … …

Write the rule.

Copy the number chain. Write the missing numbers.

**2** *2006 Progress Test level 3*

Here is a grid with some numbers shaded.

| | | | |
|---|---|---|---|
| 1 | 2 | 3 | 4 |
| 5 | 6 | 7 | 8 |
| 9 | 10 | 11 | 12 |
| | | | |

The grid continues.
Will the number 35 be shaded?
Write **Yes** or **No**. Explain your answer.

**3**   *2003 level 3*

Here is part of a calendar.

Tyrone's birthday is on December 18th.

On what day of the week is his birthday?

| December |
| Mon | Tue | Wed | Thu | Fri | Sat | Sun |
|-----|-----|-----|-----|-----|-----|-----|
|     |     | 1   | 2   | 3   | 4   |     |
| 6   | 7   | 8   | 9   | 10  |     |     |
| 13  | 14  | 15  |     |     |     |     |
| 20  | 21  | 22  |     |     |     |     |
| 27  | 28  |     |     |     |     |     |

**4**   *2003 level 3*

Look at these prices.

What is the total cost of:

a   two rulers and one pencil?

b   three blue pens?

| Ruler | 30p |
|-------|-----|
| Pencil | 15p |
| Blue pen | 35p |
| Green pen | 40p |
| Eraser | 20p |

**5**   *2005 level 3*

Copy and complete these calculations to make them correct.

Use **different numbers** each time.

$$\ldots \times \ldots = 24$$

$$\ldots \times \ldots = 24$$

$$\ldots \times \ldots = 24$$

**6**   *2006 level 3*

Work out $37 \times 5$.

# Angles and symmetry

**This unit will help you to:**

- identify and draw lines of symmetry;
- draw the reflection of a shape in a mirror line;
- use the four compass points to give and follow directions;
- recognise and draw right angles.

## 1 Symmetry

This lesson will help you to draw lines of symmetry.

 **Did you know that...?**

You can find symmetrical patterns in nature and in man-made objects.

Each half of the pattern is a reflection of the other half.

A shape that you can fold so that two halves match has a **line of symmetry**.

Some shapes have more than one line of symmetry.

A shape with a line of symmetry is **symmetrical**.

The line is called a **mirror line.**

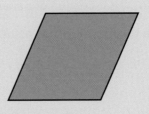

One of the lines of symmetry for the rectangle and star is shown here.

The rhombus has no lines of symmetry.

You will need a mirror.

1  Write the number of lines of symmetry for each shape.

a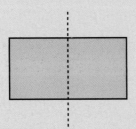

b

c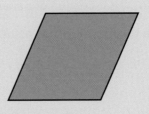

d

e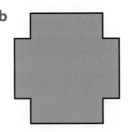

f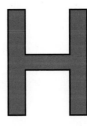

g

h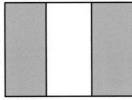

i

2  a  Draw a shape that has two lines of symmetry.

b  Draw a shape with one line of symmetry.

c  Draw a shape that has no lines of symmetry.

**3** Here are some national flags.

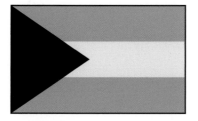

A **Bahamas**

B **Djibouti**

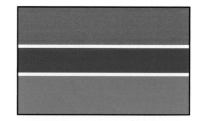

C **Gambia**

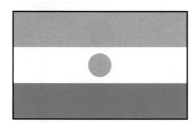

D **Niger**

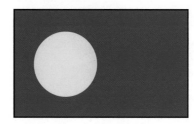

E **Palau**

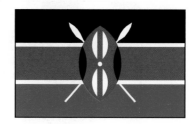

F **Kenya**

**a** Which flags have a horizontal line of symmetry?

**b** Which flags have a vertical line of symmetry?

**4** Work with a partner. You will need a computer and the program **Symmetry searcher**.

Choose a shape. Drag it onto the grid.

Where do you think it has a line of symmetry?

To check:

◉ click twice to create a line; drag the line into position;

◉ click 'Fold' and watch the shape fold over.

Drag the shape to the correct box.

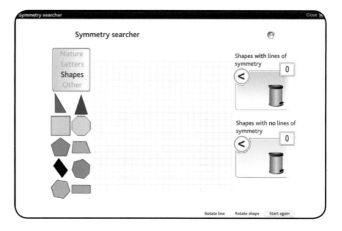

## Points to remember

⊙ If you can fold one half of a shape exactly on top of the other half, the fold line is a **line of symmetry**.

⊙ Shapes that can be folded in half in more than one way have more than one line of symmetry.

⊙ Some shapes have no lines of symmetry.

## 2 More symmetry

This lesson will help you to reflect shapes in a mirror line.

### Exercise 2

Where is the symmetry in these tiling patterns?

You will need some squared paper, scrap paper, glue and scissors for this exercise.

1. Copy each pattern on squared paper.
   Draw its reflection in the mirror lines. Check it with a mirror.

   **a**
   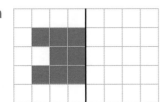

   **b**
   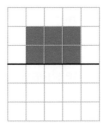

   **c**
   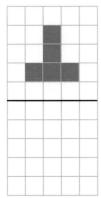

   **d**
   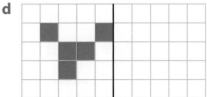

**2** **a** Fold a piece of paper in half. Cut out these shapes.

Guess what the shapes will look like before you open them out.
Open out the shapes. Stick them in your book.

**b** Fold a piece of paper in half twice.
Cut out these shapes from the corner with two folds.

Guess what the shapes will look like before you open them out.
Open them and stick them in your book.

**3** Copy each pattern on squared paper.
Reflect it in the mirror line. Check with a mirror.

**a**
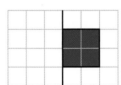

**b**
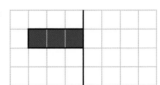

**c**
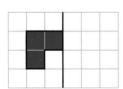

**d**
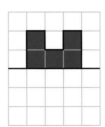

**e**
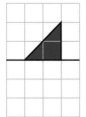

**4** Work with a partner. You will need a computer and the program **Line symmetry**.

Click on the pattern button.
Make a pattern by clicking on different squares.

Choose a mirror line.
Reflect your pattern.

Change the mirror line.
Watch how your pattern changes when the mirror line changes.

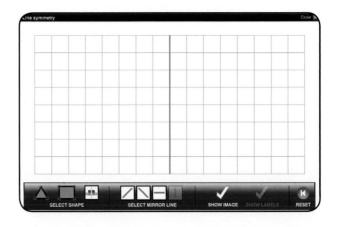

## Extension problem

**5** Copy each pattern on squared paper.

Reflect it in the mirror line. Check with a mirror.

a
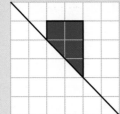

b
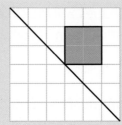

c
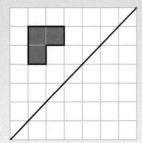

d
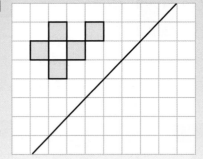

## ⊙ Points to remember

- When you reflect a shape in a mirror line, the reflection is the same size and shape as the original object.
- The shape and its reflection make a symmetrical pattern, with the mirror line as a line of symmetry.

# 3 Angles

This lesson will help you to recognise and draw right angles.

A **full turn** is four right angles.

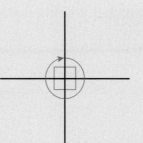

A **half turn** is two right angles.

Two right angles form a **straight line**.

A quarter turn is a **right angle**.

A right angle is marked on diagrams with a small square.

You can use a set square:

○ to draw right angles, and

○ to check if an angle is a right angle.

You will need plain paper, a ruler, pencil and set square.

# Did you know that...?

A **spirolateral** is formed by drawing a sequence of straight lines. The angle of turn after each line is always the same.

Spirolaterals were first described in 1973 by an American teacher, Frank Odds.

This is a **1, 2, 3, 4 spirolateral**.

Start at the red dot.

Draw a 1 cm vertical line.
Use the set square. Draw a right angle to turn right.

Draw a 2 cm line.
Draw a right angle to turn right.

Draw a 3 cm line.
Draw a right angle to turn right.

Draw a 4 cm line.
Draw a right angle to turn right.

Keep repeating the instructions.

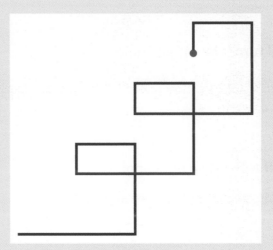

Work in a group of three or four.

1. Draw these spirolaterals.

   **a**  a 1, 2 pattern

   **b**  a 1, 2, 3 pattern

   **c**  a 1, 4 pattern

2. Try some more spirolaterals of your own. What shapes can you make?

3. What is the spirolateral that is shown on the right?

4. Which spirolaterals return to their starting point?

5. Make a poster to show what you have found out.

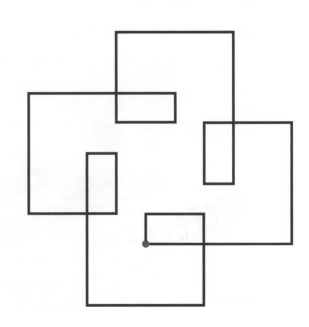

# Extension problem

Work with a partner. You will need a computer and the program **Logo**.

6 You can draw spirolaterals on a computer using Logo.

A turtle on the screen draws a path.

To tell the turtle to turn right, use the command RT 90.

Some useful commands are:

CS      Clear the screen

FD 50    Go forward 50 steps

RT 90    Turn right through a right angle

LT 90    Turn left through a right angle

Make sure you put spaces in the correct places.

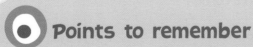 Points to remember

⊙ A **full turn** is four right angles.

⊙ A **half turn** is two right angles or a straight line.

⊙ You can use a **set square** to draw and check right angles.

## 4 Moving on a grid

This lesson will help you to move around a grid using a compass and instructions.

### Exercise 4

The four main compass points are north, south, east and west.

You can use these to give directions.

### Example

Describe the route from A to B.

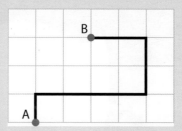

The route from A to B is:

1 unit north

4 units east

2 units north

2 units west

---

① Play **Find your way** with a partner.

You need two dice, each a different colour, squared paper, a ruler and two coloured pencils.

One dice tells you how many centimetres to move. The other tells you the direction.

#### Rules

⊙ Mark points A and B far apart on the paper. Draw a compass rose in a corner.

⊙ Take turns to roll the two dice.

⊙ Draw your route from A using your coloured pencil. If you would go off the paper, roll again.

⊙ The winner is the first to get to B.

On the direction dice:

1 North

2 South

3 East

4 West

5 Choose a direction

6 Miss a turn

**2** Write directions for the route from START to STOP.

**a**

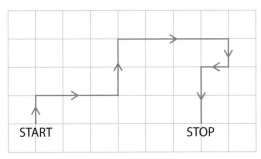

**b**

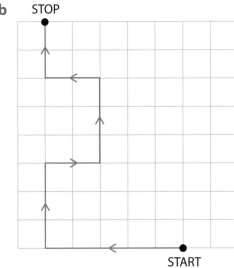

**3** Mark a point A in the centre of a 10 × 10 square on squared paper.
Draw a small compass rose in one corner.

**a** Draw this route.

    North 4 units

    West 3 units

    South 6 units

    East 7 units

    North 2 units

**b** Mark the end point B. Write one instruction to get directly from A to B.

**4** Look at this drawing.

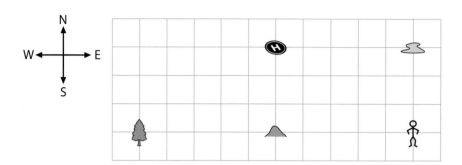

**a** What is west of the pond?

**b** What is north of the hill?

**c** If you are at the hill, which object is to the east?

**d** If you are at the hill, which object is to the west?

**e** Ajit says that the tree is south of the helipad marked with H. Is he right? Why?

## Extension problem

**5** A robot makes these moves from a point X.

3 units north

2 units west

1 unit south

5 units east

4 units north

2 units west

6 units south

**a** The robot needs to return to X in one move.
Write the instruction.

**b** Make up a puzzle like this for your partner. Solve each other's puzzles.

## Points to remember

⊙ The four main compass points are **north**, **east**, **south** and **west**.

⊙ Compass points are used to give directions.

# How well are you doing?

**Can you:**

- identify and draw lines of symmetry?
- draw the reflection of a shape in a mirror line?
- use the four compass points to give and follow directions?
- recognise and draw right angles?

(1) *2006 level 3*

Look at each shape.

a
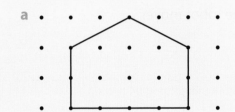

i   Is this shape a quadrilateral?

ii  Does it have at least one right angle?

b
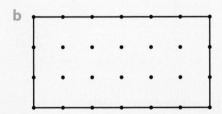

i   Is this shape a quadrilateral?

ii  Does it have at least one right angle?

c
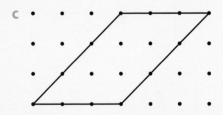

i   Is this shape a quadrilateral?

ii  Does it have at least one right angle?

d
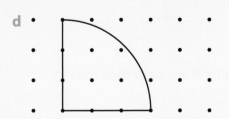

i   Is this shape a quadrilateral?

ii  Does it have at least one right angle?

A robot moves on a square grid.

The grid is 4 m by 4 m.

The robot can move north, south, east or west.

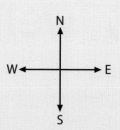

Example:

**Grid**

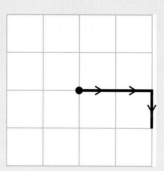

**Directions**

The robot started at ●

It moved 1 m east, then it moved 1 m east, then it moved 1 m south.

**a** Copy the grid. Draw lines on it to show where the robot moves.

Start at ●

Move 1 m **north**, then

move 1 m **west**.

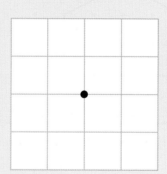

**b** Copy and complete the directions to show how the robot could move from ● to ■.

Start at ●

Move 1 m ......, then

move 1 m ......, then

move 1 m ......

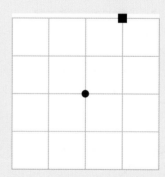

**c** Now write a different set of directions to show how the robot could move from ● to ■.

**③** *2004 level 3*

Copy the diagram below on squared paper.

Complete the shape to make it symmetrical about the mirror line. Use a ruler.

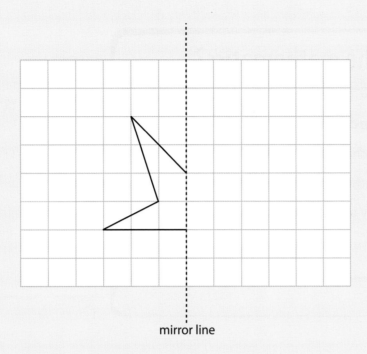

mirror line

**④** *2003 level 3*

The letter D has a line of symmetry.

Which of the other letters have a line of symmetry?

# D   M   E   S   N

# Functional skills 2

## Where is the mathematics?

**This group activity will help you to:**

- ◉ look for mathematics around you;
- ◉ think of mathematical questions to ask;
- ◉ choose how to present answers.

## Background

Mathematics is all around us.

Looking for the maths in pictures will help you to understand how widely maths is used.

## Problem 1

**What mathematical questions could you ask about this picture?**

What answers would you give?

## Problem 2

**What mathematical questions could you ask about this picture?**

What answers would you give?

**What mathematical questions could you ask about this picture?**

What answers would you give?

**Problem 4**

**What mathematical questions could you ask about this picture?**

What answers would you give?

Be prepared to discuss your questions and answers with other groups.

# Multiplying and dividing

**This unit will help you to:**

◉ double and halve numbers;

◉ remember the 2, 3, 4, 5 and 10 times tables;

◉ develop the 6 and 8 times tables;

◉ multiply and divide, using a calculator when appropriate;

◉ find remainders and round answers up or down.

## 1 Doubling and halving

This lesson will help you to double and halve numbers.

 **Did you know that...?**

Identical twins are said to be the double of each other.

One twin sometimes calls the other 'my other half'.

The double of any whole number is always even.

### Exercise 1

**Example 1**

Double 48.

$48 = 40 + 8$

| | **40** | **8** |
|---|---|---|
| double | 80 | 16 |

$80 + 16 = 96$

Split 48 into **40 + 8**.

Double 40 to get 80.
Double 8 to get 16.

Add 80 and 16.          **Answer: 96**

**Example 2**

Halve 72.

$72 = 70 + 2$

| | **70** | **2** |
|---|---|---|
| halve | 35 | 1 |

$35 + 1 = 36$

Split 72 into **70** + **2**.

Halve 70 to get 35.

Halve 2 to get 1.

Add 35 and 1.     **Answer: 36**

Do these **without a calculator**. Show your working.

**1** You need a copy of this table on **N1.3 Resource sheet 1.1**.

| Half | 2 | | 4 | | | 7 | | | 13 | | | |
|---|---|---|---|---|---|---|---|---|---|---|---|---|
| **Number** | 4 | 10 | | | 24 | | 46 | | | | 16 | |
| **Double** | 8 | | | 12 | | | | 44 | | 72 | | 96 |

Complete the table on the resource sheet.

**2** **a** Caitlin makes a sequence. Her rule is 'find half the last number then add 5'.

90    50    30    …    …

What are the two missing numbers in her sequence?

**b** The rule for this sequence is 'double the last number then subtract 3'.

4    5    7    …    …

What are the two missing numbers in her sequence?

**c** In this sequence each number is double the previous number.

…    …    12    24    48    …

What are the three missing numbers?

**3** Use doubling to work these out. Show your working.

**a** $19 \times 2$    **b** $38 \times 2$    **c** $47 \times 2$    **d** $15 \times 4$

**e** $17 \times 4$    **f** $23 \times 4$    **g** $11 \times 8$    **h** $25 \times 9$

**4** Draw two rings.

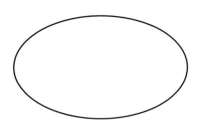 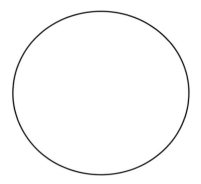

Use each of the numbers **10**, **20**, **30**, **40** and **50** once.

Write the numbers in the rings.

The total of one ring must be half the total of the other ring.

There are three ways to do it. Find them all.

## Extension problem

**5** Choose a number from 10 to 50.

Make a chain.

### Rules

 If the number is even, halve it.

 If the number is odd, add 1.

 Keep going.

What happens?

Try more numbers.
What did you discover?

**Example:**  Start with **28**.

| | |
|---|---|
| **28** | halve it |
| **14** | halve it |
| **7** | add 1 |
| **8** | halve it |
| **4** | halve it |
| **2** | halve it |
| **1** | add 1 |

## ⦿ Points to remember

- **Doubling** is the same as multiplying by 2.
- **Halving** is the same as dividing by 2.
- To multiply by 4, double and double again.
- To multiply by 8, double, double again and double again.

## 2 Sixes and eights

This lesson will help you get to know the six and eight times tables.

 **Did you know that...?**

Times tables have been around for 4000 years.

The **Sumerians** lived in Babylon in what is now Iraq. The picture is a drawing of Babylon.

They carved times tables on damp clay tiles. They then baked the tiles until they were hard.

They did this in an oven or in the sun.

400 old tiles with times tables on were found in Iraq in 1854.

### Exercise 2

Numbers in the **six times table** are multiples of **6**.

| 0 | 1 | 2 | 3 | 4 | 5 | 6 | 7 | 8 | 9 |
|---|---|---|---|---|---|---|---|---|---|
| 10 | 11 | 12 | 13 | 14 | 15 | 16 | 17 | 18 | 19 |
| 20 | 21 | 22 | 23 | 24 | 25 | 26 | 27 | 28 | 29 |
| 30 | 31 | 32 | 33 | 34 | 35 | 36 | 37 | 38 | 39 |
| 40 | 41 | 42 | 43 | 44 | 45 | 46 | 47 | 48 | 49 |
| 50 | 51 | 52 | 53 | 54 | 55 | 56 | 57 | 58 | 59 |
| 60 | 61 | 62 | 63 | 64 | 65 | 66 | 67 | 68 | 69 |
| 70 | 71 | 72 | 73 | 74 | 75 | 76 | 77 | 78 | 79 |

| 0 | 1 | 2 | 3 | 4 | 5 | 6 | 7 | 8 | 9 |
|---|---|---|---|---|---|---|---|---|---|
| 10 | 11 | 12 | 13 | 14 | 15 | 16 | 17 | 18 | 19 |
| 20 | 21 | 22 | 23 | 24 | 25 | 26 | 27 | 28 | 29 |
| 30 | 31 | 32 | 33 | 34 | 35 | 36 | 37 | 38 | 39 |
| 40 | 41 | 42 | 43 | 44 | 45 | 46 | 47 | 48 | 49 |
| 50 | 51 | 52 | 53 | 54 | 55 | 56 | 57 | 58 | 59 |
| 60 | 61 | 62 | 63 | 64 | 65 | 66 | 67 | 68 | 69 |
| 70 | 71 | 72 | 73 | 74 | 75 | 76 | 77 | 78 | 79 |

Numbers in the **eight times table** are multiples of **8**.

Do these **without a calculator.** Show your working.

1. Write the answers.

a $6 \times 2$     b $2 \times 8$     c $3 \times 6$     d $3 \times 8$     e $6 \times 4$

f $4 \times 8$     g $5 \times 6$     h $8 \times 5$     i $6 \times 6$     j $8 \times 6$

k $7 \times 6$     l $8 \times 7$     m $6 \times 9$     n $8 \times 8$     o $8 \times 0$

(2) Use two of these numbers each time.

 **3**    **5**    **7**    **6**    **8**

Copy and complete these.

a ...... × ...... = 30    b ...... × ...... = 15

c ...... × ...... = 24    d ...... × ...... = 35

e ...... × ...... = 40    f ...... × ...... = 56

g ...... × ...... = 21    h ...... × ...... = 18

(3) These numbers are the multiples of 8 from 8 to 80.
Two are missing. Which two are they?

56    24    40    8    80    64    16    32

(4) Chews cost 6p and lollipops cost 8p.

What do these cost?

a  3 chews                    b  4 lollipops

c  5 lollipops and 2 chews    d  3 lollipops and 2 chews

(5) Play **Sixes** with a partner.
You need two dice. Each spot is worth **6**.

## Rules

⊙ Each player draws a 2 by 3 grid.

⊙ Take turns to roll the dice.

⊙ Write your score in a box.

⊙ Carry on until all the boxes are full.

⊙ Now take turns to roll the dice again.

⊙ If your score is on your grid, cross it out. If not, wait for your next turn.

⊙ The winner is the first to cross out all their numbers.

If you play again, make each spot worth **8**.

**6** In this grid,
6 is the product of 2 and 3,
16 is the product of 8 and 2,
and so on.

| × | 2 | 8 |
|---|---|---|
| 3 | 6 | 24 |
| 2 | 4 | 16 |

Copy and complete this grid.

| × | 2 | 3 | 4 | 5 |
|---|---|---|---|---|
| 6 | | | | |
| | 16 | | | |

**7** Copy and complete these. Put 6 or 8 in each box.

a  32 = ☐ + ☐ + ☐ + ☐ + ☐

b  34 = ☐ + ☐ + ☐ + ☐ + ☐

c  36 = ☐ + ☐ + ☐ + ☐ + ☐

d  38 = ☐ + ☐ + ☐ + ☐ + ☐

## Extension problem

**8** What is the total score on each dartboard?

a

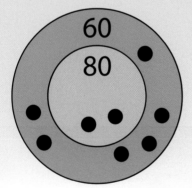

b

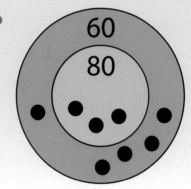

## Points to remember

⊙ Answers in the 6 times table are double the 3 times table.

**Example:** seven 3s are 21, so seven 6s are double 21 or 42.

⊙ Answers in the 8 times table are double the 4 times table.

**Example:** fives 4s are 20, so five 8s are double 20 or 40.

# 3 Multiplication

This lesson will help you to multiply numbers, using a calculator when needed.

## Exercise 3

You can multiply numbers using a grid.

### Example

Calculate 34 × 4.

First, estimate the answer. It will be a bit more than 30 × 4 = 120.

34 = 30 + 4          Split 34 into **30 + 4**.

| × | 30 | 4 |
|---|-----|----|
| 4 | 120 | 16 |

Make a grid.
Multiply 30 by 4 to get 120
Multiply 4 by 4 to get 16

120 + 16 = 136          Add 120 and 16.

**Answer: 136**

Do questions 1 to 3 **without a calculator**. Show your working.

1   Work these out.

   a  78 × 5          b  69 × 4          c  47 × 3

   d  56 × 2          e  85 × 3          f  28 × 5

2   Find the cost of these.

   a   Two packets of sweets at 12p each.

   b   Three cans of drink at 29p each.

   c   Six tins of paint at £14 each.

   d   Four DVDs at £13 each.

   e   Three grapefruit at 24p each.

   f   Five oranges at 19p each.

**3** Solve these problems.

**a** The shop is open for 6 days each week.
It is open for 14 hours each day.

How many hours is the shop open each week?

**b** One length of the swimming pool is 28 metres.
Abigail swims 5 lengths of the pool.

How far does Abigail swim altogether?

**c** A bus ticket costs 58p.
How much do 4 of the bus tickets cost?

**d**  Sam has 5 glasses.
He pours 175 ml milk into each glass.

Altogether, how much milk does Sam pour into the glasses?

**4** Play **Make the least** with a partner.
You need a dice and a calculator.
Each player should draw three boxes like this.

**Rules**

◉ One of you rolls the dice.

◉ Each of you secretly writes the score in one of your boxes.
No changes can be made afterwards.

◉ Do this twice more.

◉ Now work out your answers **without the calculator**.

◉ **Use the calculator** to check.

◉ The player with the smallest answer scores 1 point.

◉ The winner is the first to get 3 points.

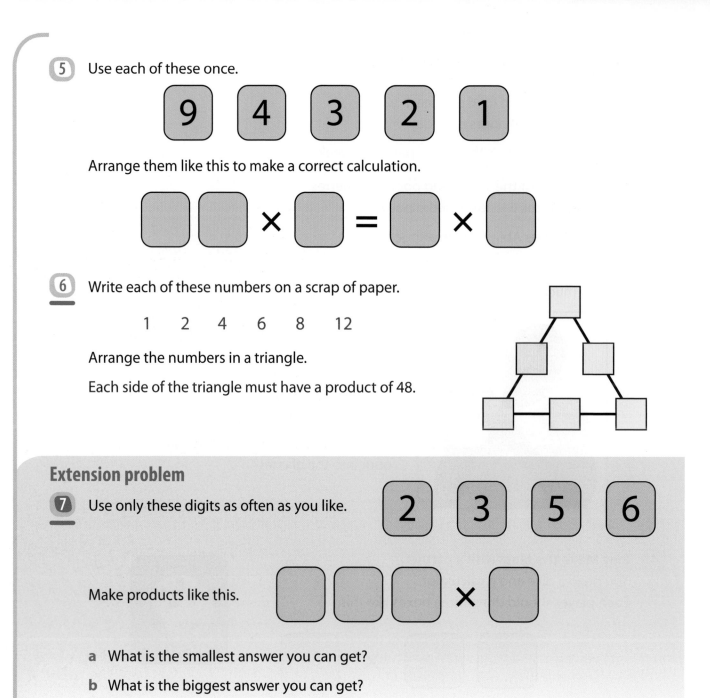

**5** Use each of these once.

9 4 3 2 1

Arrange them like this to make a correct calculation.

⬜⬜ × ⬜ = ⬜ × ⬜

**6** Write each of these numbers on a scrap of paper.

1 2 4 6 8 12

Arrange the numbers in a triangle.

Each side of the triangle must have a product of 48.

## Extension problem

**7** Use only these digits as often as you like.

2 3 5 6

Make products like this. ⬜⬜⬜ × ⬜

a What is the smallest answer you can get?

b What is the biggest answer you can get?

## ⦿ Points to remember

⊙ Use a grid to do TU × U and a calculator for bigger numbers.
⊙ Read problems carefully.
⊙ Write down the sum you will do.
⊙ Do the sum. Use a calculator if allowed. Show your working.
⊙ Check your answer is about the right size.
⊙ Record your answer, with the units.

## 4 Division and remainders

This lesson will help you to divide numbers and find remainders, using a calculator when needed.

### Exercise 4

This multiplication square shows the facts in some of the multiplication tables.

Look down the column for **3**. Look across the row for **6**. You can see that **3 × 6 = 18**.

| × | 1 | 2 | 3 | 4 | 5 | 6 | 8 | 10 |
|---|---|---|---|---|---|---|---|----|
| 1 | 1 | 2 | 3 | 4 | 5 | 6 | 8 | 10 |
| 2 | 2 | 4 | 6 | 8 | 10 | 12 | 16 | 20 |
| 3 | 3 | 6 | 9 | 12 | 15 | 18 | 24 | 30 |
| 4 | 4 | 8 | 12 | 16 | 20 | 24 | 32 | 40 |
| 5 | 5 | 10 | 15 | 20 | 25 | 30 | 40 | 50 |
| 6 | 6 | 12 | 18 | 24 | 30 | 36 | 48 | 60 |
| 8 | 8 | 16 | 24 | 32 | 40 | 48 | 64 | 80 |
| 10 | 10 | 20 | 30 | 40 | 50 | 60 | 80 | 100 |

### Example

What is the remainder when you divide 32 by **6**?

Look down the column for **6**.
32 lies between 30 and 36.
You can see that 5 × 6 = 30, or five 6s are 30.

So when 32 is divided by 6, the answer is 5 remainder 2.
Another way to write this is 32 ÷ 6 = 5 R 2.

Do these **without a calculator**.

1. Write only the answers.

    a  15 ÷ 3　　　b  12 ÷ 4　　　c  20 ÷ 5　　　d  8 ÷ 4

    e  12 ÷ 2　　　f  16 ÷ 4　　　g  18 ÷ 6　　　h  21 ÷ 3

    i  35 ÷ 5　　　j  32 ÷ 4　　　k  18 ÷ 2　　　l  28 ÷ 4

2. Write only the remainder.

    a  19 ÷ 3　　　b  14 ÷ 4　　　c  28 ÷ 5　　　d  43 ÷ 4

    e  96 ÷ 10　　　f  17 ÷ 2　　　g  25 ÷ 3　　　h  32 ÷ 6

**3** Look at these numbers.

15    10    7    12

  **a** Which have no remainder when you divide them by 2?

  **b** Which have no remainder when you divide them by 3?

  **c** Which have no remainder when you divide them by 4?

  **d** Which have no remainder when you divide them by 5?

**4** Solve these problems. Show your working.

  **a** There are 83 marbles in a bag.
    They are packed in boxes of 10 marbles.
    How many marbles are left in the bag?

  **b** 19 marbles are shared between some children.
    Each child gets 6 marbles and there is 1 marble left over.
    How many children share the marbles?

  **c** A bag has 90 marbles in it.
    4 children take 20 marbles each.
    How many marbles are left in the bag?

**5** The number in each square is the product of the numbers in the two circles on each side of it.

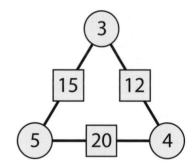

Copy and complete these.

  **a** Use 2, 3, 6           **b** Use 3, 5, 10           **c** Use 4, 8, 5

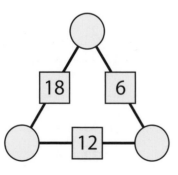
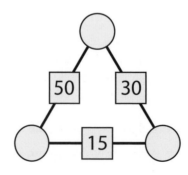
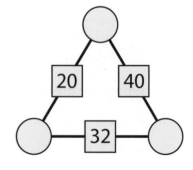

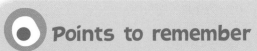

## Points to remember

- **Division** is sharing, or forming equal groups.
- $17 \div 5$ is 3 remainder 2.
  - The **divisor** is 5, the number you divide by.
  - The **quotient** is 3, the result.
  - The **remainder** is 2.

## 5 Dividing bigger numbers

This lesson will help you to divide numbers, using a calculator when needed.

### Exercise 5

**Example**

Calculate $57 \div 4$.

This means work out how many 4s there are in 57.

Estimate first. Work out:

**10** fours are **40**
**20** fours are **80**
**40** and **80** trap the number 57.

This tells you that between **10** and **20** fours make 57.

$57 = 40 + 17$          Split 57 into **40** + 17.

| × | | |
|---|---|---|
| 4 | 40 | 17 |

Make a grid.

| × | 10 | 4 | R 1 |
|---|----|---|-----|
| 4 | 40 | 17 | |

Divide 40 by 4 to get **10**, because 10 fours make 40.
Divide 17 by 4 to get **4 R 1**, because 4 fours make 16,
and there is 1 left over.

$\mathbf{10} + \mathbf{4} = 14$          Add 10 and 4.
The answer is **14 R 1**.

Do these **without a calculator**. Show your working.

(1) Work these out.

  **a** 75 ÷ 5          **b** 87 ÷ 3          **c** 64 ÷ 4

  **d** 58 ÷ 3          **e** 89 ÷ 5          **f** 98 ÷ 6

(2) This is a link.

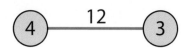

Multiply the numbers in the circles
to give the number on the link.

Copy and complete these links.

**a** (7) —— ? —— (3)     **b** (5) —— 10 —— (?)     **c** (?) —— 30 —— (5)

**d** (3) —— 21 —— (?) —— 28 —— (?)

**e** (?) —— 18 —— (?) —— 36 —— (4)

(3) Play **Remainders** with a partner.
You need a dice and two packs of digit cards from 1 to 9.
Shuffle the cards. Put face down in a pile.

### Rules

◉ Take turns.

◉ Roll the dice. If you roll 1, it counts as 10.

◉ Draw two cards.
  Make a two-digit number.
  For example, with 6 and 3 you could make 36 or 63.

◉ Divide your number by your dice score.
  The remainder is the number of points that you win for that round.
  If the remainder is zero, you get no points!

◉ The winner is the first to get 20 points.

**4**  **a**  Zoe needs 26 cartons of juice for her party.
There are 3 cartons in a pack.
How many packs does she need to buy?

**b**  Ayesha has 96 cm of ribbon to tie up presents.
She decides to cut 30 cm pieces.
How many pieces can she cut off?

**c**  Party poppers are sold in packs of 6.
Zoe wants 50 party poppers.
How many packs should she buy?

**d**  10 people can sit at one table.
43 people will be at the party.
How many tables are needed?

**e**  There are 37 children at the party.
They need teams of 5 for a game.
How many teams can they make?

**f**  There are 92 balloons in a box.
There are 4 colours of balloon.
There is the same number of each colour.
How many of each colour are there?

## Extension problem

**5**  You may **use your calculator**.

**a**  Rashid saved for a holiday in the USA.
The holiday cost £702.
Rashid saved the same amount each week.
He saved for 18 weeks.
How much did Rashid save each week?

**b**  Megan also saved for a holiday.
She saved £9 a week for 39 weeks.
What did her holiday cost?

**c**  How much more was the cost of
Rashid's holiday than Megan's holiday?

## Points to remember

- When you divide, estimate the answer first.
- Split up the number you are dividing to make it easy to divide.
- Record carefully what you do.
- Check the answer makes sense. Decide whether to round it up or down.
- Include units in your answer.

# How well are you doing?

## Multiplying and dividing (no calculator)

**1** *2003 level 3*

Hayley makes a sequence of numbers.

Her rule is: 'Find half the last number then add 10.'

Copy Hayley's sequence. Write the next two numbers.

36    28    24    …    …

**2** *1995 level 3*

a Brenda's hoops landed on the Hoopla like this:

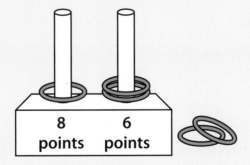

How many points did Brenda score altogether?

b Farid scored exactly 22 points.

How many hoops on the 8 points peg?

How many hoops on the 6 points peg?

**3** *2002 level 3*

a Multiply 56 by 3

b Divide 130 by 5

**4** Look at this multiplication table.

| × | 11 | 12 | 13 | 14 | 15 |
|---|----|----|----|----|----|
| 6 | 66 | 72 | 78 | 84 | 90 |
| 7 | 77 | 84 | 91 | 98 | 105 |
| 8 | 88 | 96 | 104 | 112 | 120 |
| 9 | 99 | 108 | 117 | 126 | 135 |

Use the table to copy and complete these.

a  9 × 13 = ......

b  15 × ...... = 90

c  108 ÷ 9 = ......

d  16 × 8 = ......

## Multiplying and dividing (calculator allowed)

**5**  *2000 level 3*

a  Multiply 69 by 14, then add 34.

b  Add 94 to half of 778.

c  How much less than 1000 is 59 × 16?

**6**  *2002 Progress Test level 3*

Rachel likes going to the theatre.

Each time she goes she pays for one ticket and one programme.

| Ticket | Programme |
|--------|-----------|
| £18.45 | £2.50 |

In one year Rachel goes to the theatre 13 times.

Altogether, how much does she pay?
Show your working.

# Graphs and charts 1

**This unit will help you to:**

- collect, show and interpret data in
  - lists and tables;
  - tally charts;
  - bar charts;
  - pictograms.

## 1 Lists and tables

This lesson will help you to use data in lists and tables.

### Exercise 1

Here are some examples of lists and tables.

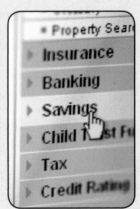

1 Look at this list of numbers:

7, 22, 13, 19, 11, 9, 15, 12, 14, 5, 26, 20, 8, 7, 14, 13,

18, 7, 8, 9, 8, 7, 5, 7, 23, 25, 16, 11, 7, 27, 10, 8

a How many numbers are there altogether in the list?

b What is the biggest number in the list?

c What is the smallest number?

2. Use the list of numbers in question 1.

Copy this table. Write each number in the right place in the table.

| Numbers with a 2 in them | Numbers with no 2 in them |
|---|---|
| | |

3. Here is a list of prices in a restaurant.

| | |
|---|---|
| Chicken curry.................................. | £4.50 |
| Spaghetti bolognaise ................... | £4.20 |
| Roast dinner .................................. | £4.60 |
| Vegetable bake............................... | £3.80 |
| Apple pie and custard.................. | £2.25 |
| Fruit salad and ice cream............ | £2.50 |

a Which is the most expensive item on the list?

b Which is the cheapest item on the list?

c Pick a main meal and a pudding. Write them down.
What do they cost altogether?

d Pick another main meal and pudding. Write them down.
What do they cost altogether?

e How much more is a roast dinner than a vegetable bake?

4. This is a table of names:

| | | | |
|---|---|---|---|
| Annabel | Daniel | Clare | Karen |
| Karl | David | Durgesh | Tia |

a How many names are there in the table?

b Which name has the least number of letters?

c Two names have seven letters. Which are they?

d What is the fifth letter of the fourth name in the first row?

e What is the sixth letter of the second name in the third column?

**5** Six children played a game.

This table shows how many points they each scored:

| Name | Paige | Chris | Ali | Hakan | Georgia | Jessica |
|---|---|---|---|---|---|---|
| Points | 7 | 5 | 4 | 6 | 9 | 2 |

  **a** Who scored the most points?

  **b** Who scored 5 points?

  **c** Which players scored more points than Hakan?

  **d** How many points did the children score altogether?

  **e** What is the difference between the highest score and the lowest score?

## Extension problem

 **Did you know that...?**

The Mayans ruled in ancient Mexico.

This table shows how the Mayans wrote numbers with dots and dashes.

A dot was 1 and a dash was 5.

They also had a zero.

| 0 | 1 | 2 | 3 | 4 |
|---|---|---|---|---|
| 5 | 6 | 7 | 8 | 9 |
| 10 | 11 | 12 | 13 | 14 |
| 15 | 16 | 17 | 18 | 19 |
| 20 | 21 | 22 | 23 | 24 |
| 25 | 26 | 27 | 28 | 29 |

**6** Look at the table of Mayan numbers. Write the Mayan number in:

  **a** the 3rd column of the 4th row      **b** the 2nd row of the 5th column

  **c** the 1st column of the 5th row      **d** the 6th row of the 4th column

 **Points to remember**

⊙ You can use **lists** and **tables** to collect and organise information.

## 2 Tally charts

This lesson will help you to use and interpret tally charts.

### Exercise 2

This person is making a **tally chart**.

Each **tally mark** stands for one item.

Every fifth **tally mark** goes across the previous four.

This makes it easier to count the number of marks. You can count them in fives.

|||| stands for 5.

|||| ||| stands for 8.

The total number of tally marks is the **frequency**.

1 Write the numbers for these tallies.

   a |||||                    b ||                    c |||| ||||
   d |||| |||| ||||           e |||| ||||             f |||| |||| ||||

2 Draw tallies for these numbers.

   a 7                    b 16                    c 3
   d 9                    e 5                     f 18

3 This tally chart shows the colour of hair of some pupils in a class.

| Hair colour | Tally | Frequency |
|---|---|---|
| black | |||| ||| | |
| brown | |||| |||| || | |
| blonde | |||| | | |
| red | | | |

   a Write down the frequency for each hair colour.

   b How many pupils are there in the class?

   c Which hair colour is the least common?

④ This is a list of some pupils' favourite colours:

green, blue, purple, pink, black, green, purple, blue, blue, red, purple, pink, blue, green, blue, pink, green, green, purple, green, blue, pink, blue

a Copy this tally chart.

| Colour | Tally | Frequency |
|--------|-------|-----------|
| green | | |
| blue | | |
| purple | | |
| pink | | |
| black | | |
| red | | |

Count the colours. Make the tally marks on your chart.

b Work out the frequency for each colour. Write it on your chart.

⑤ This is a list of the food some pupils had for breakfast:

toast, toast, cereal, toast, sandwich, cereal, egg, toast, cereal, cereal, fruit, nothing, cereal, toast, cereal, nothing

a Copy this tally chart.

| Food | Tally | Frequency |
|------|-------|-----------|
| toast | | |
| cereal | | |
| sandwich | | |
| egg | | |
| fruit | | |
| nothing | | |

Work through the list of foods and fill in the tallies on your chart.

b Work out the frequency for each food. Write on your chart.

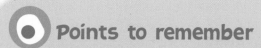

**Points to remember**

⊙ A **tally chart** helps you to sort and count data.

⊙ Each **tally mark** stands for one item.

⊙ Draw the tallies in groups of five.

⊙ The total for the tally is the **frequency**.

## 3 Bar charts

This lesson will help you to draw and interpret bar charts.

### Exercise 3

The **tally chart** and **bar chart** show the same information about the eye colours of 40 adults.

| Eye colour | Tally | Frequency |
|------------|-------|-----------|
| blue | IIII IIII II | 12 |
| hazel | IIII III | 8 |
| brown | IIII IIII IIII | 15 |
| green | IIII | 5 |

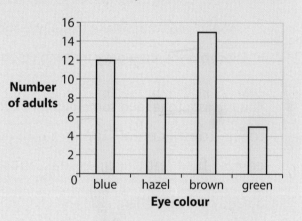

You will need squared paper, coloured pencils, a sharp pencil and a ruler.

① This tally chart shows the hair colour of some pupils.

 a Draw a bar chart to show this data.

 Make the bars 1 cm wide.
 Make the gaps 1 cm wide.

 Number the vertical axis from 0 to 12 using 1 cm for each unit.

 b Which bar is the tallest?

 c Which bar is the shortest?

 d Which bar is for 6 people?

| Hair colour | Tally | Frequency |
|-------------|-------|-----------|
| black | IIII III | 8 |
| brown | IIII IIII II | 12 |
| blonde | IIII I | 6 |
| red | I | 1 |

**2** This table shows what some pupils had for breakfast.

a Draw a bar chart to show the data.

Make the bars 1 cm wide.
Make gaps of 1 cm between them.

Number the vertical axis in 1s from 0 to 8.
Use 1 cm for each unit.

b Which is the tallest bar?

c Which bars are the same height?

d Which bar is for 5 people?

| Food | Frequency |
|---|---|
| toast | 5 |
| cereal | 6 |
| sandwich | 1 |
| egg | 1 |
| fruit | 1 |
| nothing | 2 |

**3** This table shows the favourite colours of some pupils.

a Draw a bar chart to show the data.

Make the bars 1 cm wide.
Make gaps of 1 cm between them.

Number the vertical axis in 2s from 0 to 20.
Use 1 cm for two units.

b Which is the tallest bar?

c Which is the shortest bar?

d Which bar is for 16 people?

| Colour | Frequency |
|---|---|
| green | 16 |
| blue | 8 |
| purple | 10 |
| pink | 4 |
| black | 20 |
| red | 8 |

## Extension problem

**4** 75 people were asked to name their favourite drink.

a Draw a bar chart to show the data.

Make the bars 1 cm wide.
Make gaps of 1 cm between them.

Number the vertical axis in 5s.

b Write two sentences to explain
what the bar chart shows.

| Drink | Frequency |
|---|---|
| fruit juice | 15 |
| tea | 20 |
| coffee | 10 |
| fizzy drink | 25 |
| water | 5 |

## Points to remember

In a **bar chart**:

- ⊙ both axes have labels;
- ⊙ all bars are the same width;
- ⊙ the length of the bar is the frequency;
- ⊙ there is a gap between the bars;
- ⊙ the bars can be horizontal or vertical.

## 4 Pictograms

This lesson will help you to draw and interpret pictograms.

### Exercise 4

### Example

This pictogram shows what 26 people chose as their favourite outing.

**Favourite outing**

| | | Key |
|---|---|---|
| theme park | ♀ ♀ ♀ ⸗ | ♀ stands for 2 people |
| zoo | ♀ ♀ | |
| park | ⸗ | |
| cinema | ♀ ♀ ♀ | |
| fairground | ♀ ♀ ♀ ♀ | |

The pictogram has a key to show how many people each symbol represents.

The pictogram shows that:

- ◔ 7 people chose the theme park as their favourite outing;
- ◔ only 1 person chose the park;
- ◔ the most popular outing was the fairground which was chosen by 8 people.

You will need squared paper and a sharp pencil.

**1** This table shows some pupils' favourite subjects.

   **a** Draw a pictogram to show this data.

      Use a book as the symbol for one person.

   **b** Which subject is the most popular?

| Subject | Frequency |
|---------|-----------|
| maths | 3 |
| english | 2 |
| PE | 4 |
| art | 5 |
| music | 1 |
| science | 1 |

**2** This table shows the favourite superhero of some young children.

   **a** Draw a pictogram to show the data.

      Choose a symbol to stand for one person.

   **b** Which superhero is the most popular?

| Superhero | Frequency |
|-----------|-----------|
| Spiderman | 7 |
| Superman | 4 |
| Batman | 3 |
| Ninja turtles | 1 |

**3** This table shows some pupils' favourite snacks.

| Snack | Frequency |
|-------|-----------|
| fruit | 4 |
| crisps | 4 |
| nuts | 2 |
| biscuits | 1 |
| sweets | 3 |

   **a** Draw a pictogram to show this data.

      Choose a symbol to stand for one person.

   **b** Which snack food is the least popular?

   **c** How many more pupils like fruit than biscuits as a snack?

This table shows some pupils' favourite fruit.

| Fruit | Frequency |
|-------|-----------|
| apple | 6 |
| pear | 3 |
| banana | 7 |
| grapes | 2 |
| other | 4 |

**a** Draw a pictogram to show this data.

Choose a symbol to stand for **two** people.

**b** How many more pupils liked bananas than grapes?

**c** Write two sentences to explain what the pictogram shows.

## Points to remember

⊙ You can use a **pictogram** to represent data.

⊙ The pictogram must have a key to show how many items each symbol represents.

⊙ The symbols should be the same size.

⊙ The symbols should line up neatly.

# How well are you doing?

**Can you:**

- represent and interpret data in:
  - tally charts?
  - bar charts?
  - pictograms?

**1** *2005 Progress Test level 3*

Ben recorded the number of words in the titles of books.

The tally chart shows his results.

| **Titles of books** | |
|---|---|
| one word | 卌 |
| two words | 卌 IIII |
| three words | 卌 卌 II |
| four words | 卌 卌 |
| five words | 卌 I |
| six or more words | 卌 III |

a How many books had titles with four words?

b Altogether, how many books had titles with fewer than three words?

c What was the most common number of words in the title?

Class 6 did a survey of their favourite types of story book. Here are their results.

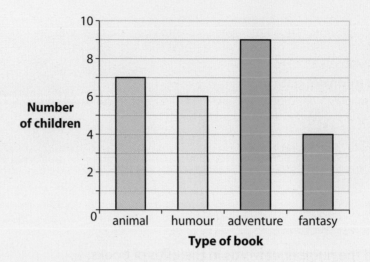

a   How many more children chose adventure books than fantasy books?

b   Five girls chose animal books. How many boys chose animal books?

③ *2003 level 3*

Kiz asked each child in his class:

> 'What kind of television programme do you prefer to watch?'

Here are his results.

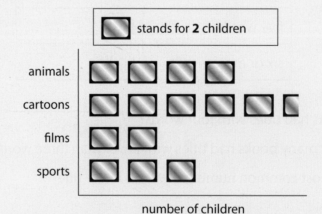

How many more children prefer to watch cartoons than films?

# Mentalcalculations

## This unit will help you to:

- do sums in your head;
- multiply and divide by 10 or 100;
- remember the 2, 3, 4, 5 and 10 times tables;
- work out facts for the 7 and 9 times tables;
- solve problems.

## 1  Quick ways to add and subtract

This lesson will show you some quick ways to add and subtract in your head.

### Did you know that...?

**Charles Dodgson**, who died in 1898, was the real name of **Lewis Carroll**, who wrote *Alice in Wonderland*.

Charles was tall, with curly brown hair and blue eyes. He married his cousin Frances and had 11 children.

Charles also taught maths at Oxford University. He loved jokes, puzzles, games, tricks with numbers, mental exercises and brainteasers.

The Mad Hatter's tea party from *Alice in Wonderland*

## Exercise 1

### Quick ways of adding

| To add 9 | Add 10 then subtract 1 |
|----------|------------------------|
| To add 99 | Add 100 then subtract 1 |
| To add 90 | Add 100 then subtract 10 |

Do this exercise **without a calculator**.

**1** Write the answers.

| | | | |
|---|---|---|---|
| **a** 45 + 9 | **b** 38 + 9 | **c** 85 + 9 | **d** 57 + 9 |
| **e** 43 − 9 | **f** 91 − 9 | **g** 55 − 9 | **h** 86 − 9 |

**2** Write the answers.

| | | | |
|---|---|---|---|
| **a** 53 + 99 | **b** 126 + 99 | **c** 432 + 99 | **d** 227 + 99 |
| **e** 138 − 99 | **f** 267 − 99 | **g** 815 − 99 | **h** 734 − 99 |

**3** Write the answers.

| | | | |
|---|---|---|---|
| **a** 86 + 90 | **b** 24 + 90 | **c** 517 + 90 | **d** 328 + 90 |
| **e** 561 − 90 | **f** 482 − 90 | **g** 388 − 90 | **h** 271 − 90 |

**4** Write the answers.

| | | | |
|---|---|---|---|
| **a** 28 + 52 | **b** 46 + 32 | **c** 28 + 62 | **d** 13 + 42 |
| **e** 78 − 52 | **f** 67 − 32 | **g** 96 − 62 | **h** 71 − 42 |

**5** Write the answers.

| | | | |
|---|---|---|---|
| **a** 45 + 39 | **b** 54 + 29 | **c** 76 + 19 | **d** 38 + 59 |
| **e** 78 − 29 | **f** 67 − 39 | **g** 96 − 79 | **h** 83 − 49 |

**6** Play **Fifteens** with a partner.

Copy this grid and the numbers.

The first player uses 1, 3, 5, 7 and 9.
The second player uses 2, 4, 6 and 8.

Each number can be used only once.

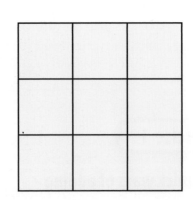

**Rules**

- Take turns.

1 3 5 7 9     2 4 6 8

- Write one of your numbers on the grid.
  Cross out the number you used

- The winner is the first to get a line of three numbers with a sum of 15.

**7** You need some digit cards from 1 to 8.

Arrange the cards in a square like this.
It has a hole in the middle.

Make each side of the square add up to 12.

Record your square in your book.

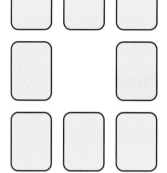

---

## Extension problems

**8** Which two pins would score:

a  23       b  26       c  21

Which three pins would score:

d  31       e  34       f  26

**9** What scores can you get with four pins?

There are five possibilities.
Try to find them all.

---

### ◉ Points to remember

- When you add several small numbers, look for pairs that sum to 10, or near doubles.
- Use quick ways to add and subtract, e.g.
  - to add 9, add 10 then subtract 1;
  - to subtract 9, subtract 10 then add 1;
  - to add 99, add 100 then subtract 1;
  - to subtract 99, subtract 100 then add 1;
  - to add 90, add 100 then subtract 10;
  - to subtract 90, subtract 100 then add 10.
- Make jottings if you need to.

# 2 Adding and subtracting two-digit numbers

This lesson will help you to add or subtract two-digit numbers in your head.

## Exercise 2

### Example 1

Here are two different ways to do $27 + 45$ in your head.

$27 + 45$

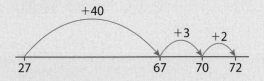

**Answer: 72**

**Method 1**

Start with 27.

Add 40 to make 67.

You have 5 more to add.

Bridge through 70, so add 3 to make 70.

Add the last 2 to make 72.

$27 + 45$

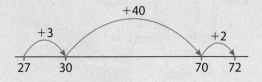

**Answer: 72**

**Method 2**

Start with 27.

Bridge through 30, so add 3 to make 30.

You have 42 more to add.

Add 40 to make 70.

Add the last 2 to make 72.

### Example 2

Here are two different ways to do $82 - 57$ in your head.

$82 - 57$

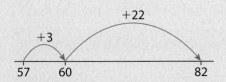

**Answer: 25**

**Method 1**

Count up from 57 to 82.

Bridge through 60, so add 3 to make 60.

Add 22 to make 82.

Altogether you have added $22 + 3 = 25$.

$82 - 57$

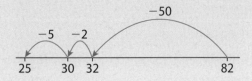

**Answer: 25**

**Method 2**

Count back 57 from 82.

Start with 82. Count back 50 to make 32.

Count back 2 more to make 30.

You have counted back 52 so far,

so count back the last 5 to make 25.

Do this exercise **without a calculator**.

**1** Write the answers. Make jottings if you need to.

    **a**   23 + 58            **b**   38 + 24            **c**   45 + 43

    **d**   38 + 46            **e**   57 + 68            **f**   49 + 68

    **g**   36 + 76            **h**   45 + 78            **i**   76 + 89

**2** Write the answers. Make jottings if you need to.

    **a**   26 − 13            **b**   38 − 21            **c**   47 − 24

    **d**   62 − 36            **e**   91 − 16            **f**   43 − 29

    **g**   23 − 14            **h**   54 − 29            **i**   55 − 37

**3** Choose from these numbers.

Copy and complete:

    **a**   … + … = 51        **b**   … − … = 11        **c**   … − … = 41

    **d**   … + … = 74        **e**   … + … = 92        **f**   … − … = 29

    **g**   … − … = 13        **h**   … + … = 63        **i**   … + … = 75

    **j**   … − … = 5

## Extension problem

**4** Write the answers. Make jottings if you need to.

    **a**   178 + 67      **b**   217 − 53      **c**   342 + 75      **d**   672 − 46

## Points to remember

- An empty number line helps you to do sums in your head.
- To add, start with the larger number.
- To subtract, count up from the smaller to the larger number.
- Jump through multiples of 10.
- If two numbers add up to 100, the units add up to 10 and the tens add up to 9.

## 3 Missing number sums

This lesson will help you to solve missing number problems.

### Exercise 3

Subtraction 'undoes' addition and addition 'undoes' subtraction.

### Example

I think of a number. I add 58 and get 92. What is my number?

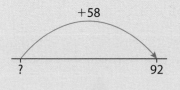

Represent the problem on a number line.

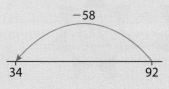

Now work backwards.

Start with 92. Subtract 58. The answer is 34.

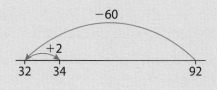

You can do this in two steps if you want to.

Do these **without a calculator**.

1. Raj subtracts 14 from his number. He gets 29. What is his number?

2. I add 37 to my number. I get 64. What is my number?

3. I think of a number. I add it to 57. The answer is 86. What is my number?

4. I think of a number. I take it from 87. The answer is 34. What is my number?

5. I subtract 158 from my number. The answer is 60. What is my number?

6. I add 123 to my number. I get 160. What is my number?

7. I think of a number. I add it to 45. The answer is 91. What is my number?

8. I think of a number. I subtract it from 36. The answer is 9. What is my number?

9. I double my number. The answer is 56. What is my number?

10. I halve my number. The answer is 47. What is my number?

**11** Copy and complete:

**a** $42 + \square = 97$     **b** $\square + 36 = 81$     **c** $38 + \square = 65$

**d** $71 - \square = 26$     **e** $\square - 41 = 19$     **f** $53 - \square = 36$

**12** Play **Make it up** with a partner.
You need two dice, two pens in different colours
and a copy of the grid on **N1.4 Resource sheet 3.1**.

| 95 | 94 | 92 | 91 | 90 | 88 |
|----|----|----|----|----|----|
| 85 | 84 | 82 | 80 | 76 | 75 |
| 70 | 64 | 60 | 50 | 40 | 0 |

**Rules**

⊙ Take turns.

⊙ Roll both dice. The 1 on a dice counts as **10**.

⊙ Multiply the two numbers.

⊙ Work out what to add to make 100.

⊙ If you see the answer on the grid, cross it out with your coloured pen.
If the answer is already crossed out, wait for your next turn.

⊙ Carry on until all the numbers are crossed out.

⊙ The winner is the player who crosses out most numbers.

**13** Copy and complete:

**a** $32 \times \square = 64$     **b** $\square \times 5 = 100$     **c** $25 \times \square = 75$

**d** $120 \div \square = 12$     **e** $\square \div 10 = 10$     **f** $45 \div \square = 5$

## Extension problems

**14** I add 1 to my number, then double it.
The answer is 46. What is my number?

**15** I halve my number, then subtract 5.
The answer is 20. What is my number?

## Points to remember

⊙ Adding is the inverse of subtracting.

⊙ Multiplying is the inverse of dividing.

⊙ To solve 'missing number' problems, use a number line.

# 4 Introducing thousands

This lesson will help you to use numbers in the thousands.

## Exercise 4

The number 2845 in words is

two thousand, eight hundred and forty-five.

$2845 = 2000 + 800 + 40 + 5$

| Thousands | Hundreds | Tens | Units |
|---|---|---|---|
| 2 | 8 | 4 | 5 |

### Example

Write in order: 72, 678, 8040, 405. Start with the smallest.

The smallest number is **72** because it has only **7 tens** and 2 units.

678 and 405 both contain hundreds, tens and units.
405 has **4 hundreds** so this is the next number.
678 has **6 hundreds** so this is the next number.

8040 has **8 thousands** so this is the largest number.

The order is 72, 405, 678, 8040.

① Write in thousands, hundreds, tens and units:

    **a** 2315      **b** 6483      **c** 1267      **d** 4207      **e** 5076

② Write as a number:

    **a** 400 + 50 + 8      **b** 800 + 90 + 3      **c** 1000 + 200 + 30 + 4

    **d** 2000 + 500 + 40 + 7      **e** 2000 + 300 + 8      **f** 5000 + 9

③ What is:

    **a** the value of **6** in the number 13**6**5?      **b** the value of **5** in the number 4**5**89?

    **c** the value of **3** in the number **3**070?      **c** the value of **9** in the number 837**9**?

④ Write in words:

    **a** 85      **b** 269      **c** 6248      **d** 4081      **e** 2103

(5) Write in figures:

a four hundred and eighty five

b five thousand, two hundred and sixty-seven

c eight hundred and four

d four thousand and twenty-one

e six thousand and eight.

(6) Here are four cards.

a Use all the cards.
Make the biggest possible number.

b Use all the cards.
Make the smallest possible number.

c Make a number between
3000 and 3500.

(7) Play **Smaller and smaller** with a friend.
You need two packs of digit cards from 0 to 6.

**Rules**

◉ Shuffle all the cards. Put them face down on the table.

◉ Take turns to pick a card until you have four cards each.

◉ Each player makes the smallest possible number with their four cards.

◉ The player with the smallest number wins a point.

◉ Put the cards back face down. Shuffle them and pick again.

◉ The winner is the first to get 5 points.

**Extension problems**

(8) Write to the nearest 10:

a 48          b 56          c 75          d 98

(9) Write to the nearest 100:

a 459          b 768          c 317          d 450

**10** Write to the nearest 1000:

a 3400      b 4870      c 2410      d 6500

 **Points to remember**

⊙ You can write 7853 as 7000 + 800 + 50 + 3.

⊙ To put numbers in order, look at the digits from the left.

## 5 Multiplying and dividing by 10 or 100

This lesson will help you to multiply or divide by 10 or 100.

### Exercise 5

When you **multiply** a number:

     by **10**, its digits move **1 place to the left**;

     by **100**, its digits move **2 places to the left**;

When you **divide** a number:

     by **10**, the digits move **1 place to the right**;

     by **100**, the digits move **2 places to the right**.

**Examples**

$56 \times 10 = 560$

$56 \times 100 = 5600$

$2300 \div 10 = 230$

$2300 \div 100 = 23$

Do these **without a calculator**.

1 Copy and complete:

     a $46 \times 100 = \ldots$          b $25 \times 10 = \ldots$

     c $50 \times 10 = \ldots$          d $90 \times 100 = \ldots$

     e $56 \times \ldots = 560$          f $53 \times \ldots = 530$

     g $40 \times \ldots = 4000$          h $10 \times \ldots = 1000$

2 Copy and complete:

     a $720 \div 10 = \ldots$          b $3760 \div 10 = \ldots$

     c $8300 \div 100 = \ldots$          d $5000 \div 100 = \ldots$

     e $550 \div \ldots = 55$          f $9100 \div \ldots = 910$

     g $4300 \div \ldots = 43$          h $8000 \div \ldots = 800$

(3) Copy and complete:

a  2050 ÷ 10 = …

b  7000 ÷ 100 = …

c  51 × … = 5100

d  205 × 10 = …

e  8000 ÷ 100 = …

f  450 ÷ … = 45

(4) Mr Brown does gardening.

He is paid £10 an hour.

a  How much is he paid for 35 hours?

b  In one weekend Mr Brown earned £150.

How many hours of gardening did he do?

(5) This is what you need to make one chocolate cake.

## 1 chocolate cake

| | |
|---|---|
| 300 g | flour |
| 150 g | sugar |
| 200 g | butter |
| 120 g | chocolate |
| 4 | eggs |

Write a list of what you need to make 10 chocolate cakes.

(6) a  Laura has £30. How much is this in pence?

b  Oliver changes 400p into pounds. How many pounds does he get?

c  Daniel has fifty 10p coins. How much is this in pounds?

d  Razia has £25 in 10p coins. How many 10p coins does she have?

**7** a Rhys has 20 metres of string.
   He cuts it into 100 centimetre pieces.

   How many pieces does he cut?

   b Imogen has 10 metres of string.
   She cuts it into 10 centimetre pieces.

   How many pieces does she cut?

**8** Jasmine pours out 5 litres of juice.
   She pours 100 ml of juice into each glass.

   How many glasses of juice does she pour?

 **Points to remember**

⊙ When a number is:
   × 10, its digits move 1 place to the left;
   × 100, its digits move 2 places to the left.
⊙ When a number is:
   ÷ 10, the digits move 1 place to the right;
   ÷ 100, the digits move 2 places to the right.

## 6 Working out new facts

This lesson will help you to work out new facts from facts you already know.

### Exercise 6

You can often use the facts that you know to work out other facts.

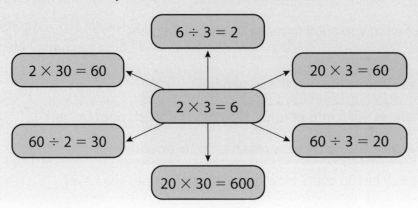

$6 \div 3 = 2$

$2 \times 30 = 60$   $20 \times 3 = 60$

$2 \times 3 = 6$

$60 \div 2 = 30$   $60 \div 3 = 20$

$20 \times 30 = 600$

Do these **without a calculator**.

① Write the answers.

a  70 × 2      b  80 × 3      c  60 × 5      d  90 × 3

e  50 × 4      f  90 × 4      g  160 ÷ 2      h  350 ÷ 5

i  120 ÷ 4      j  150 ÷ 3      k  180 ÷ 3      l  200 ÷ 4

② Use only these numbers.

20      40      120      200

Copy and complete:

a  … × **2** = …        b  … ÷ **2** = …        c  … × **3** = …

d  … ÷ **3** = …        e  … × **6** = …        f  … ÷ **6** = …

g  … × **5** = …        h  … ÷ **5** = …        i  … × **10** = …

③ Draw the diagram. Look at the fact in the middle.

Write a new fact that you can work out from it at the end of each arrow.

a

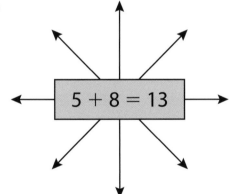

5 + 8 = 13

b

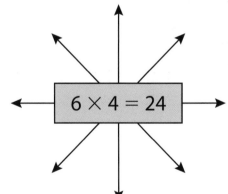

6 × 4 = 24

### Points to remember

⊙ You can work out new facts by:
  – using facts that you already know;
  – using patterns;
  – using inverse operations.

This lesson will help you to work out the 7 and 9 times tables.

### Exercise 7

**Patterns in the 9 times table**

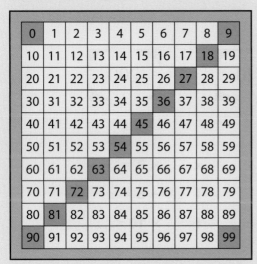

**10 times** a number **minus the number** is **9 times** a number.

**Example**

| ten 3s | minus | 3 | equals | nine 3s |
|---|---|---|---|---|
| 10 × 3 | – | 3 | = | 9 × 3 |
| 30 | – | 3 | = | 27 |

| ten 5s | minus | 5 | equals | nine 5s |
|---|---|---|---|---|
| 10 × 5 | – | 5 | = | 9 × 5 |
| 50 | – | 5 | = | 45 |

**Patterns in the 7 times table**

**5 times** a number **plus 2 times** the number is **7 times** a number.

**Example**

| five 3s | plus | two 3s | equals | seven 3s |
|---|---|---|---|---|
| 5 × 3 | + | 2 × 3 | = | 7 × 3 |
| 15 | + | 6 | = | 21 |

| five 5s | plus | two 5s | equals | seven 5s |
|---|---|---|---|---|
| 5 × 5 | + | 2 × 5 | = | 7 × 5 |
| 25 | + | 10 | = | 35 |

Do these **without a calculator**. Show your working.

1　Write the answers.

　　a　7 × 2　　　b　2 × 9　　　c　3 × 7　　　d　3 × 9　　　e　7 × 4

　　f　4 × 9　　　g　5 × 7　　　h　8 × 9　　　i　6 × 7　　　j　9 × 9

**2** Use two of these numbers each time.

 **2**   **3**   **5**   **7**  **9**

Copy and complete:

a ... × ... = 10        b ... × ... = 14

c ... × ... = 18        d ... × ... = 35

e ... × ... = 45        f ... × ... = 21

g ... × ... = 63        h ... × ... = 27

**3** Which of these are multiples of 7?

45    14    27    42    54    49    15    28

**4** CDs cost £7 and DVDs cost £9.

What do these cost?

a 3 CDs                 b 4 DVDs

c 2 CDs and 5 DVDs      d 6 CDs and 3 DVDs

e 7 CDs and 6 DVDs      f 5 CDs and 7 DVDs

**5** Play **Nines** with a partner.
You need two dice. Each spot is worth **9**.

### Rules

◎ Each player draws a 2 by 3 grid.

◎ Take turns to roll the dice.
Write your score in a box.

◎ Carry on until all the boxes are full.

◎ Now take turns to roll the dice again.

◎ If your score is on your grid, cross it out. If not, wait for your next turn.

◎ The winner is the first to cross out all their numbers.

If you play again, make each spot worth **7**.

**6** Look at these numbers.    1    2    3    4    5    6    7

Max crosses out one of the numbers.
The rest of the numbers add up to a multiple of 5.

Which number does Max cross out?

## Extension problem

**7** Copy and complete this multiplication table.

| × | 2 | | 7 |
|---|---|---|---|
| | | 15 | 35 |
| 9 | | | |
| | 20 | | |

---

## ⦿ Points to remember

- ⊙ 9 times a number is 10 times a number minus the number.
- ⊙ 7 times a number is 5 times a number plus 2 times the number.

---

## 8 Puzzles

This lesson will help you to solve number puzzles and problems.

### ⓘ Did you know that...?

**Theuth** was the ancient Egyptian god of numbers, sums, draughts and dice.

A game that Theuth was thought to have made up was **Five stones** or **Jacks**. This game is played all over the world.

You throw a stone in the air and pick up more stones before you catch it.

Or you toss one stone, then two, then three, and so on, and catch them on the back of your hand.

When you solve a problem, read it carefully. Talk it through with a partner.

Make sure that you are clear about what you need to do.

1  a  Pete the Pirate has five piles of gold bars.
      He can move one or more bars at a time.

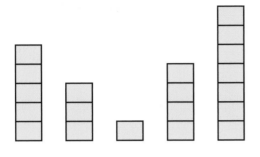

Pete moves the bars so that each
pile has the same number.

What is the least number of moves he can make?

   b  Pete puts his 20 gold bars in four piles of bars.
      Each pile has 2 more bars than the one before it.

      How many bars are there in each pile?

2  Jake is also a pirate. He has 20 bags of gold.
   He has put them in four treasure chests.

   The first chest has 4 more bags than the second chest.
   The second chest has 1 less bag than the third chest.
   The fourth chest had twice as many bags as the second chest.

   How many bags are there in each chest?

3  Kate has less than 50 CDs in her car.

   She counted them in sixes.
   She had 4 left over.

   She counted them in fives.
   She had 3 left over.

   How many CDs does Kate keep in her car?

4 Dan has less than 50 books.

Dan counted his books in fives.
He had three left over.

He counted them in sevens.
He had five left over.

How many books does Dan have?

**Extension problem**

 5 Draw two rings.

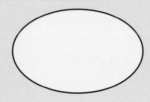  

Look at these numbers.

4    5    6    7    8

Write each number in one of your rings.

The sum of the numbers in each ring must be the same.

## Points to remember

- Read problems carefully.
- Decide what you are asked to do.
- Work systematically.
- It may help to draw a diagram or make a table.
- Look for patterns and relationships.

# How well are you doing?

## Mental calculations (no calculator)

**1**  *2006 level 3*

What is the missing number on each number line to move from 0 to 20?

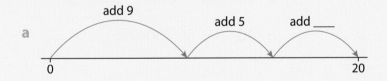

a

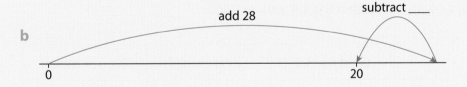

b

**2**  *2006 level 3*

a  Work out 37 + 46.

b  What number do you need to add to 63 to make 100?

c  What number do you need to subtract from 100 to make 38?

**3** *2004 Progress Test level 3*

    **a** The numbers on these cards should have a total of 50.

       What is the missing number?

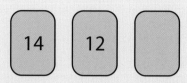

    **b** The numbers on these cards should have a total of 50.

       What could the two missing numbers be?

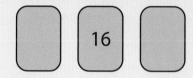

**4** *2006 Progress Test level 3*

What number could go in the box to make the calculation correct?

    **a** $3 + 11 = 4 + \square$         **b** $15 + 8 = 5 + \square$

    **c** $40 - 10 = 50 - \square$       **d** $30 \div 3 = 300 \div \square$

**5** *2002 level 3*

The table shows how many medals the UK won in 2000.

|  | Gold medal | Silver medal | Bronze medal |
|---|---|---|---|
| Olympics | 11 | 10 | 7 |
| Paralympics | 41 | 43 | 47 |

Altogether, the UK won more medals at the Paralympics than at the Olympics.

How many more?

Show your working.

# Measures 1

**This unit will help you to:**

- ◉ tell the time on different clocks;
- ◉ find the difference between two times;
- ◉ measure lengths using millimetres, centimetres and metres;
- ◉ know how millimetres, centimetres and metres relate to each other.

## 1 Reading time

 **Did you know that...?**

The first clocks were used about 5000 to 6000 years ago.

Sundials were the earliest clocks.

Using the Sun was later replaced by water clocks.

Water clocks are still used in some countries today.

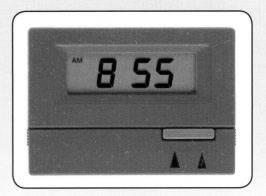

This lesson will help you to tell the time.

### Exercise 1

An **analogue** clock has hands.

This clock shows 3 o'clock.

A **digital** clock has a number display.

This clock shows 8:55 in the morning.

You will need **G1.3 Resource sheet 1.1**.

**1** Write the time.

a 　　b 　　c 　　d

e 　　f 　　g 　　h

i 　　j 　　k 　　l

**2** Draw these times on the clocks on **G1.3 Resource sheet 1.1**.

a 5 o'clock　　　　　b 1 o'clock　　　　　c 9 o'clock

d 7 o'clock　　　　　e quarter past 4　　　f quarter to 4

g five past 6　　　　h twenty to 7　　　　i twenty five to 3

j twenty past 2　　　k ten past 9　　　　l half past 12

**3** Write the times shown on these digital clocks.

a

b

c

**4** Write these as digital clock times.

a 5 o'clock

b 1 o'clock

c 9 o'clock

d 7 o'clock

e quarter past 4

f quarter to 4

g five past 6

h twenty to 7

i twenty five to 3

j twenty past 2

k ten past 9

l half past 12

**5** Draw these times on **G1.3 Resource sheet 1.1**.

a 9:00

b 1:30

c 5:15

d 10:45

e 12:05

f 4:55

g 3:10

h 8:50

i 11:20

j 7:40

k 2:25

l 6:35

## Extension problem

**6** Roughly what time does this clock show?

---

### Points to remember

- There are 60 minutes in an hour.
- The numbers on the clock face show the hours.
- They have a different value when the minute hand is pointing to them.

## 2 A long time

This lesson will help you to work out time problems.

### Exercise 2

#### Example 1

Emily and Maya are going to visit some friends.
The journey takes 1 hour 30 minutes.

They leave home at 10 o'clock.
At what time do they arrive?

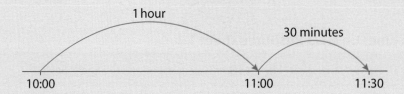

Emily and Maya arrive at 11:30.

#### Example 2

Emily and Maya leave work at 5:15.
They get home at 7 o'clock.

How long has it taken them?

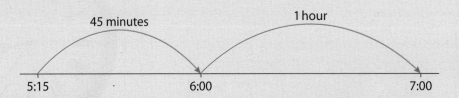

The journey takes 1 hour 45 minutes.

---

① Find the difference between these times.

a 6:45 and 8:45

b 2:30 and 3:30

c 3:15 and 3:45

d 1:15 and 2:10

e 4:40 and 5:55

f 1:10 and 3:25

g 3:25 and 4:15

h 4:05 and 6:10

i 9:20 and 11:55

j 10:35 and 12:10

② Amy's journey to work takes 25 minutes. Copy and complete this table.

| Amy leaves home | Amy arrives at work |
|:---:|:---:|
| 8:00 | |
| 7:55 | |
| 12:10 | |
| 6:45 | |
| | 9:25 |
| | 10:15 |
| | 4:45 |
| | 7:30 |

③ **a** John walks to a football match.
He leaves home at 6:25.
He gets to the ground at 7:10.

How long does his journey take?

**b** The match kicks off at 7:45.
It finishes at 9:30.

How long does the match last?

**c** John gets a lift home in a friend's car.
He leaves the ground at 9:50.
His journey home takes 20 minutes.

At what time does he get home?

④ Use some of these times to fill the gaps. The story must make sense.

3:00    6:15    4:45    4:00    7:30

Maddy got on her bike at ......... .
She got home 45 minutes later at ......... .

Then she played on her computer for 90 minutes.
She stopped at ......... .

**5** **a** This clock is 25 minutes slow.

Write the correct time.

**b** This clock is 25 minutes fast.

Write the correct time.

## Extension problems

**6** The pictures show two clocks.

Work out the difference in time between the two clocks.

 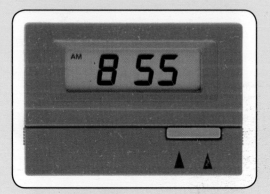

**7** The guitar lesson is longer than the drum lesson. How much longer?

Guitar lesson starts      Guitar lesson ends      Drum lesson starts      Drum lesson ends

## Points to remember

⊙ To work out a time interval, count on from the start time.

⊙ A blank time line helps you to work out a time interval.

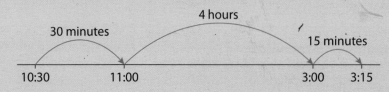

# 3 Choosing units of length

 **Did you know that...?**

The metre was fixed as the standard unit of length in 1799.

A metre bar was made from platinum and stored in Paris.

The world is 40 million metres round the Equator.

**A metre rule**

This lesson will help you to learn when to use millimetres, centimetres, metres and kilometres.

## Exercise 3

A **centimetre** is about the width of a finger nail.

You can shorten the names of units.

- ◎ **kilometre** is **km**
- ◎ **metre** is **m**
- ◎ **centimetre** is **cm**
- ◎ **millimetre** is **mm**

1  What unit would you use to measure these? Choose from:

**millimetres (mm)**     **centimetres (cm)**     **metres (m)**     **kilometres (km)**

a  The length of your classroom              b  The length of a football pitch

c  The height of this letter J               d  The length of an aeroplane

e  The distance from the Earth to the Sun    f  The width of your desk

2  Choose the measurement that makes most sense from these:

**7 millimetres   3 metres   5 kilometres   1 metre   50 kilometres   12 centimetres**

a  The height of a basketball hoop           b  The distance you can walk in an hour

c  The width of a door                       d  The width of a CD

e  The distance from London to Brighton      f  The width of a biro

**3** Write the missing unit. Choose from

> **mm    cm    m    km**

a  Peter cycles 5 ...... to school.

b  Yasmin is 135 ...... tall.

c  Sam walks 500 ...... to school.

d  This crayon is 100 ...... long.

e  The classroom is 8 ...... wide.

f  My pencil case is 20 ...... long.

g  The river is 50 ...... long.

h  The swimming pool is 150 ...... deep.

i  The postage stamp is 30 ...... wide.

j  The door handle is 1 ...... from the ground.

**4** Copy and complete this story.

Choose from these to fill in the gaps:

> **mm    cm    m    km**

Jake drove 7 ......... to buy a wardrobe.

He needed one that measured

200 ......... by 100 ......... by 300 ......... .

He bought a wardrobe.

The label said it was 2 ......... by 1 ......... by 3 .........

It was a perfect fit.

⊙ **Points to remember**

⊙ Use millimetres (mm) for very small distances, e.g. the length of an ant.

⊙ Use centimetres (cm) for small distances, e.g. the length of a book.

⊙ Use metres (m) for longer distances, e.g. the length of the school hall.

⊙ Use kilometres (km) for very long distances, e.g. the length of a river.

# 4 The metric system

The **Eiffel tower** in Paris is 324 metres high.

The **London Eye** is 135 metres high.

**Blackpool Tower** is 62 metres high.

This lesson will help you to change one unit of length to another.

## Exercise 4

1 km = 1000 m      1 m = 100 cm      1 cm = 10 mm

You can use this chart to help you change one unit of length to another.

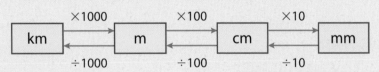

### Example 1

Change 18 cm to millimetres.

For every centimetre there are 10 millimetres.

So 18 cm is $18 \times 10 = 180$ mm.

### Example 2

Change 600 cm to metres.

For every 100 cm there is 1 metre.

So 600 cm is $600 \div 100 = 6$ m.

You may **use your calculator**.

1 Change these to millimetres.

     **a** 3 cm          **b** 4 cm          **c** 9 cm          **d** 15 cm          **e** 100 cm

**2** Change these to centimetres.

    **a** 7 m            **b** 23 m           **c** 50 m           **d** 100 m          **e** 1000 m

**3** Change these to metres.

    **a** 3 km          **b** 12 km          **c** 20 km          **d** 6 km            **e** 1000 km

**4** Change these to millimetres.

    **a** 5 cm 2 mm       **b** 9 cm 7 mm       **c** 6 cm 1 mm

**5** Change these to centimetres.

    **a** 3 m 15 cm       **b** 4 m 20 cm       **c** 8 m 91 cm

**6** Change these to metres.

    **a** 1 km 300 m     **b** 4 km 700 cm     **c** 2 km 750 m

**7** Change these to centimetres.

    **a** 90 mm         **b** 250 mm        **c** 110 mm

**8** Change these to metres.

    **a** 700 cm        **b** 9000 cm       **c** 1200 cm       **d** 6400 cm

**9** Change these to kilometres.

    **a** 9000 m        **b** 8000 m        **c** 3000 m        **d** 1000 m

## Extension problems

**10** Change these to centimetres.

    **a** 80 mm         **b** 57 m          **c** 5 m 40 cm

**11** Change these to metres.

    **a** 9100 cm       **b** 4 km          **c** 6 km 700 m

**12** Write these in order of size. Start with the smallest.

        **4 metres**      **6000 millimetres**      **500 centimetres**

## Points to remember

⊙ This chart will help you to change one unit of length to another.

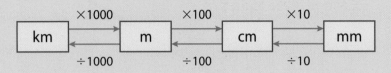

# 5 Measuring length

This lesson will help you to use a ruler or tape measure to measure lengths accurately.

## Exercise 5

To draw a straight line accurately, start at the zero mark or 0 on the ruler.

Draw along the edge of the ruler until you come to the length you need.

When you use a ruler to measure a line, put the zero mark of the ruler at the start of the line.

This line is 4 cm 6 mm long, or 46 mm long.

1. Measure each line in centimetres.

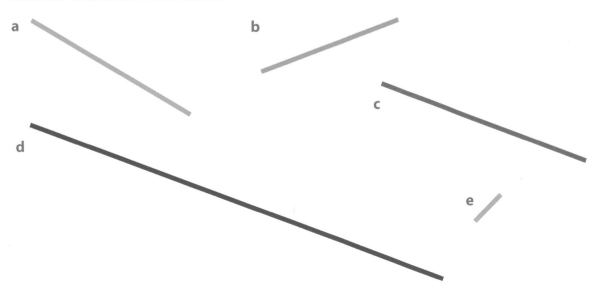

(2) Measure each line in millimetres.

(3) Draw these lines accurately.

a  7 cm          b  10 cm          c  9 cm          d  13 cm          e  1 cm

(4) Draw these lines accurately.

a  30 mm          b  60 mm          c  110 mm          d  15 mm          e  25 mm

(5) Use a tape measure or metre stick to measure these in metres and centimetres.

a  The height of the window sill in your classroom

b  The height of the door handle in your classroom

c  The length of your classroom

d  The width of your classroom

(6) Use a ruler to measure these in centimetres and millimetres.

a  The height of this textbook

b  The width of this textbook

c  The thickness of this textbook

## Extension problems

**7** You cannot see all of the key. It is 5 cm 2 mm long.

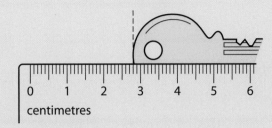

One end is at 2 cm 8 mm on the scale.
Where is the other end?

**8** The picture shows a pencil sharpener, paper clip and box of matches.

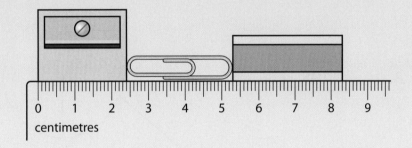

a What is the length of all three things together?
   Write your answer in millimetres.

b What is the length of the pencil sharpener?
   Write your answer in millimetres.

c What is the length of the box of matches?
   Write your answer in millimetres.

### Points to remember

⊙ When you use a ruler to measure or draw lines, position the zero mark on the ruler at the end of the line.

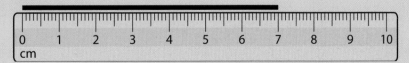

⊙ Write a length of 2 metres and 80 centimetres as 2 m 80 cm.

# How well are you doing?

① *2004 Key Stage 2 level 3*

Write the two letters to match each clock to the correct time. One has been done for you.

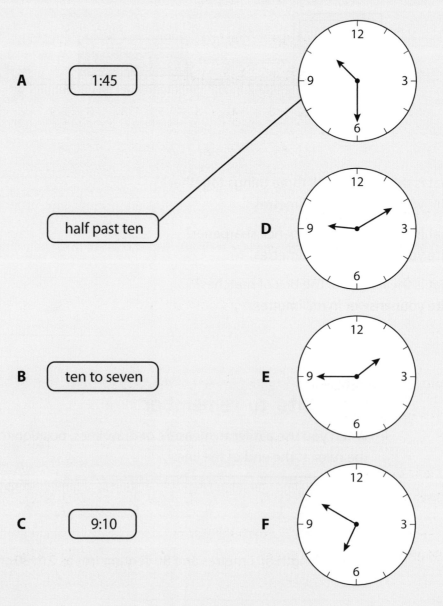

A   1:45

half past ten

B   ten to seven

C   9:10

**2** *2003 Key Stage 2 level 3*

Here is a clock.
How many minutes is it until this clock shows 7:30?

**3** *2005 Key Stage 2 level 3*

These are the radio programmes one morning.

| | |
|---|---|
| **7:00** | Music show |
| **7:55** | Weather report |
| **8:00** | News |
| **8:15** | Travel news |
| **8:25** | Sport |
| **8:45** | Holiday programme |

a Josh turns the radio on at 7:25.

How many minutes does he have to wait for the weather report?

b The Holiday programme lasts for 40 minutes.

At what time does the holiday programme finish?

**4** *2007 Progress Test level 3*

Write the letter for the best estimate for each of the following.

a The height of a door.
   A 2 mm          B 2 cm          C 2 m          D 2 km

b The length of a pen.
   A 14 mm         B 14 cm         C 14 m         D 14 km

c The distance between Leeds and Manchester.
   A 64 mm         B 64 cm         C 64 m         D 64 km

**5** *2003 KS2 level 3*

Draw a line 3 cm longer than this line.
Use a ruler.

**6** *2005 KS1 level 3*

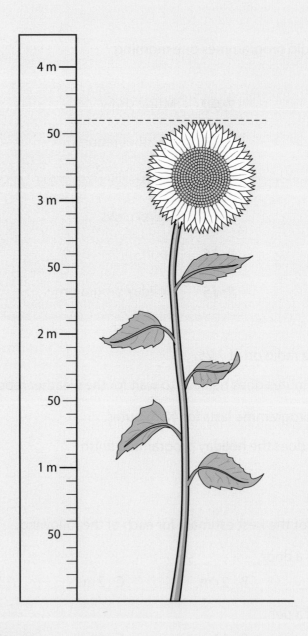

How tall is the sunflower?

Copy and complete this sentence.

The sunflower is ...... m ...... cm tall.

Here is a triangle.

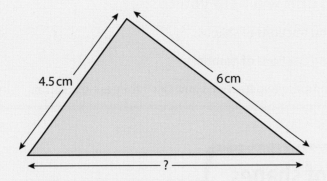

Measure the length of the longest side.

# Fractions

This unit will help you to:

- ⊙ find fractions of shapes;

- ⊙ find fractions of numbers;

- ⊙ compare two fractions and say if they are the same.

## 1 Fractions of shapes

This lesson will help you to find fractions of shapes.

### Exercise 1

This shape is divided into 5 equal triangles.

**2** out of **5** triangles are blue, so $\frac{2}{5}$ of the shape is blue.

**3** out of **5** triangles are red, so $\frac{3}{5}$ of the shape is red.

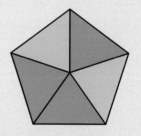

The top number shows that 2 parts of the shape are blue.

→ $\frac{2}{5}$ ←

The top number is the **numerator**.

The bottom mumber shows that the shape has 5 equal parts.

The bottom number is the **denominator**.

① Draw this rectangle.
Colour $\frac{1}{2}$ blue, $\frac{1}{4}$ red and $\frac{1}{4}$ yellow.

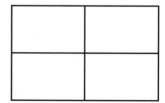

**2** What fraction of each shape is shaded?

a
b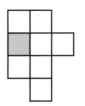
c
d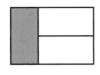

e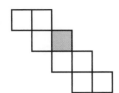
f
g
h

**3** What fraction of each shape is shaded?

a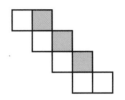
b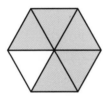
c
d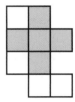

e
f
g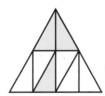
h

**4** You will need some squared paper.

a Copy this shape.
Divide it into halves.
Do it in three different ways.

b Now copy this shape.
Divide it into quarters.
Do it in three different ways.

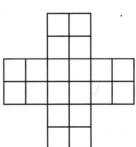

**5** Copy and complete these.

a $\frac{1}{4} + \frac{3}{4} = \ldots$

b $1 - \frac{1}{2} = \ldots$

c $\frac{4}{4} + \ldots = 1$

d $1 - \frac{1}{10} = \ldots$

e $\frac{1}{2} + 1\frac{1}{2} = \ldots$

f $\ldots + \frac{5}{6} = 1$

**6**   **a**   John drinks $\frac{3}{4}$ of a bottle of water.
        What fraction is left?

   **b**   $\frac{1}{6}$ of a pizza is pepperoni.
        What fraction is not pepperoni?

   **c**   Hasan spends $\frac{1}{2}$ of his pocket money.
        What fraction does he have left?

   **d**   Jess has a bag of sugar.
        She uses $\frac{3}{10}$ of it to make a cake.
        What fraction of the sugar is left?

   **e**   Kelly has saved $\frac{2}{3}$ of the cost of a holiday.
        What fraction of the cost does she still need to save?

## Extension problems

**7**   Estimate the fraction of each plate that is yellow.

   **a**      **b**      **c**

**8**   Copy each shape on squared paper.

   Divide each shape into halves. Each half must be exactly the same.

   **a**   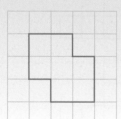   **b**      **c**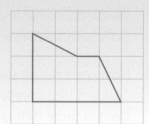

## ⊙ Points to remember

- A fraction is part of a whole.
- If a shape has 3 out of 8 equal parts shaded, then $\frac{3}{8}$ is shaded.
- The top number of a fraction is the **numerator**.
- The bottom number is the **denominator**.

# 2 Fractions of numbers

This lesson will help you to work out fractions of numbers.

 **Did you know that...?**

In the year 500, the Indians wrote numbers like this.

| 1 | 2 | 3 | 4 | 5 | 6 | 7 | 8 | 9 |
|---|---|---|---|---|---|---|---|---|
| — | = | ≡ | + | ʰ | ४ | ʔ | ↄ | ? |

The Indians were the first to write fractions a bit like we do today.

They wrote one number above another without a line between them.

For example, they wrote the fraction $\frac{4}{7}$ like this $\begin{smallmatrix}+\\7\end{smallmatrix}$.

## Exercise 2

To find $\frac{1}{2}$, divide by 2.
To find $\frac{1}{3}$, divide by 3.
To find $\frac{1}{4}$, divide by 4.

### Example 1

Find $\frac{1}{4}$ of £24.

$24 \div 4 = 6$, so $\frac{1}{4}$ of £24 is £6.

A quick way to find **one quarter** is to find **half of half**.

### Example 2

Find $\frac{1}{4}$ of £24.

Half of £24 is £12.
Half of £12 is £6.

So a quarter of £24 is £6.

1. Work these out. Show your working.

   a $\frac{1}{2}$ of 18      b $\frac{1}{4}$ of 24      c $\frac{1}{10}$ of 50

   d $\frac{1}{8}$ of 40      e $\frac{1}{3}$ of 21      f $\frac{1}{100}$ of 400

   g $\frac{1}{3}$ of 30 kg   h $\frac{1}{2}$ of 48 km   i $\frac{1}{5}$ of £45

2. a Sarah spends $\frac{1}{5}$ of her savings of £35. How much does she spend?

   b $\frac{1}{4}$ of the 32 pupils in a class wear glasses. How many of the pupils wear glasses?

(3) What fraction is shaded?

a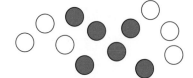

b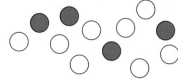

c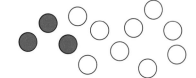

d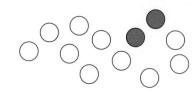

e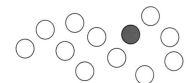

f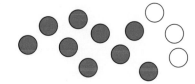

(4) **a** One half of a number is 8.
What is the number?

**b** One tenth of a number is 6.
What is the number?

**c** One quarter of a number is 3.
What is the number?

**d** One fifth of a number is 7.
What is the number?

(5) Play **Matching fractions** with a partner.

You will need a set of cards made from **N1.5 Resource sheet 2.1**.

### Rules

- Spread the cards face down on the table. Shuffle them.

- Take turns to turn over two cards.
  If they match, keep them and have another turn.

- If they don't match, turn them back face down.
  It is then the other player's turn.

- The winner is the player who wins the most pairs of cards.

## Extension problems

To find $\frac{2}{3}$, first find one third,
then multiply the result by 2.

### Example

Find $\frac{2}{3}$ of 150 grams.

$150 \div 3 = 50$, so $\frac{1}{3}$ of 150 g is 50 g.

$50 \times 2 = 100$, so $\frac{2}{3}$ of 150 g is 100 g.

**6** Work these out. Show your working.

   a $\frac{3}{5}$ of £30        b $\frac{3}{4}$ of 24 kg        c $\frac{3}{10}$ of 80 cm

   d $\frac{5}{8}$ of 40 litres      e $\frac{2}{3}$ of 60 g        f $\frac{3}{100}$ of £400

**7** Half of the pieces of fruit in the bowl are apples.
There are also 3 plums, 2 pears and one orange.
How many apples are there in the bowl?

## Points to remember

- Find fractions of numbers by dividing.
- To find $\frac{1}{3}$, divide by 3.
- To find $\frac{1}{4}$, divide by 4, or find half of one half.
- To find three quarters, work out one quarter, then multiply by 3.

## 3 Comparing fractions

This lesson will help you to know when two fractions are the same as each other.

### Exercise 3

**Equivalent fractions** are fractions that are equal.

These rectangles are all the same size.

One half of each rectangle is shaded.

  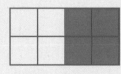

$\frac{1}{2}$        $\frac{2}{4}$        $\frac{4}{8}$

The diagrams show that $\frac{1}{2}$, $\frac{2}{4}$ and $\frac{4}{8}$ are equivalent fractions.

**1** What fraction is shaded? Write **Half** or **More than half** or **Less than half**.

  a        b        c        d        e

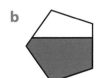  

**2** Use this fraction wall.

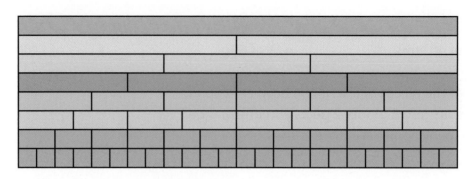

**a** Write three fractions the same as:

i $\frac{1}{2}$ ii $\frac{1}{4}$ iii $\frac{1}{3}$ iv $\frac{3}{4}$ v $\frac{2}{3}$

**b** Which fraction is bigger?

i $\frac{1}{2}$ or $\frac{5}{8}$ ii $\frac{1}{3}$ or $\frac{5}{12}$ iii $\frac{7}{8}$ or $\frac{5}{6}$ iv $\frac{1}{3}$ or $\frac{7}{24}$

**3** Use the fraction wall to help you. Copy and complete these.

**a** $\frac{1}{2} = \frac{\square}{4}$ **b** $\frac{1}{2} = \frac{\square}{8}$ **c** $\frac{1}{4} = \frac{\square}{8}$

**d** $\frac{2}{4} = \frac{\square}{8}$ **e** $\frac{3}{4} = \frac{\square}{8}$ **f** $1 = \frac{\square}{8}$

**g** $\frac{1}{2} = \frac{\square}{6}$ **h** $\frac{1}{3} = \frac{\square}{6}$ **i** $\frac{1}{2} = \frac{\square}{6}$

**j** $\frac{1}{4} = \frac{\square}{12}$ **k** $\frac{3}{4} = \frac{\square}{12}$ **l** $\frac{1}{6} = \frac{\square}{12}$

**4** The three fractions in each question are equivalent.

Which fractions are they?

**a**

 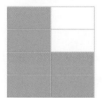 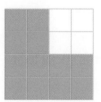

**b**

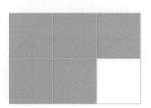  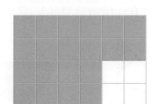

**5**  **a**  Two of these fractions have the same value. Write the two fractions.

$$\frac{5}{6} \qquad \frac{1}{3} \qquad \frac{1}{2} \qquad \frac{4}{8} \qquad \frac{2}{5}$$

**b**  Two of these fractions are greater than one half. Write the two fractions.

$$\frac{1}{8} \qquad \frac{6}{10} \qquad \frac{5}{8} \qquad \frac{3}{10} \qquad \frac{3}{9}$$

 **Points to remember**

⊙ **Equivalent fractions** are the same as each other.

⊙ Use diagrams to compare fractions.

# How well are you doing?

## Fractions (no calculator)

**1** *2002 level 3*

How much of each square grid is shaded?
For each grid, write **More than half** or **Half** or **Less than half**.

a 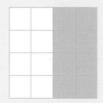  b   c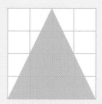

**2** *2005 Progress Test level 3*

a Which shape below has $\frac{3}{4}$ shaded?

A   B   C

D   E   F

b Amy says:

> $\frac{1}{2}$ of 20 is bigger than $\frac{1}{4}$ of 40

Is she correct? Write **Yes** or **No**. Explain how you know.

**(3)** *2007 Progress Test level 3*

Look at the shape.

What fraction of the shape is shaded?

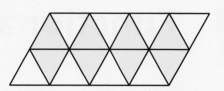

**(4)** *2003 Key Stage 2 level 3*

Which two of these fractions have the same value?

$$\frac{2}{10} \qquad \frac{1}{3} \qquad \frac{1}{2} \qquad \frac{5}{10} \qquad \frac{1}{4}$$

**(5)** *1999 Key Stage 2 level 3*

Jack ate half the cherries on the plate.

These are the cherries that were left.

How many cherries were on Jack's plate before he ate half of them?

**(6)** *1998 Key Stage 2 level 3*

What fraction of these tiles is circled?

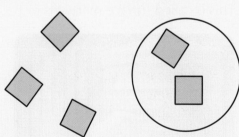

**(7)** *1997 level 3*

Sue and Ben each have 12 biscuits.

a   Sue eats a quarter of her biscuits.
    How many biscuits does Sue eat?

b   Ben eats 6 of his 12 biscuits.
    What fraction of his biscuits does Ben eat?

c   How many biscuits are left altogether?

# Functional skills 3

## Sending mail

**This group activity will help you to:**

- work out how to tackle a problem;
- choose the maths to do to solve it;
- explain your solution.

## General information

You can send mail to go by land or sea to anywhere in the world.

This is called surface mail.

On the right are the Post Office charges for surface mail from 7 April 2008.

| Weight up to | Cost |
|---|---|
| 100 g | £1.16 |
| 150 g | £1.63 |
| 200 g | £2.09 |
| 250 g | £2.55 |
| 300 g | £3.00 |
| 350 g | £3.45 |
| 400 g | £3.91 |
| 450 g | £4.36 |
| 500 g | £4.81 |

## Background

Lisa has a small business.
She posts CDs anywhere in the world.

Each parcel uses the same amount of paper.

Lisa sends two 300 g parcels.
It costs £3.00 + £3.00 = £6.00.

There is a cheaper way to send 600 g.

One 500 g parcel and one 100 g parcel costs £4.81 + £1.16 = £5.97.

## Problem

### The cheapest way to send parcels

Use the Post Office table of charges.

Work out what it costs Lisa to post each pair of parcels.

Then find a different way for Lisa to pack two parcels so it is cheaper to post them.

**1**  150 g and 150 g

**2**  250 g and 250 g

**3**  400 g and 300 g

**4**  250 g and 200 g

**5**  200 g and 150 g

**6**  400 g and 250 g

**7**  250 g and 150 g

**8**  300 g and 250 g

**9**  400 g and 400 g

Be ready to compare your ideas with other groups.

# Graphs and charts 2

**This unit will help you to:**

- draw and use:
  - tally charts;
  - frequency tables;
  - bar charts;
  - pictograms.
  - Venn and Carroll diagrams.

## 1 Tally charts and frequency tables

This lesson will help you to learn about tally charts and frequency tables.

### Exercise 1

In a **tally chart** each tally mark stands for one item.

Every fifth mark is drawn across the previous four.
This makes it easy to count the tally marks in groups of five.

The **frequency** is the total number.

### Example

This tally chart shows the number of types of trees in a park.

| Tree | Tally | Frequency |
| --- | --- | --- |
| ash | ⦀⦀ ||| | 8 |
| rowan | ⦀⦀ || | 7 |
| oak | ⦀⦀ ⦀⦀ ⦀⦀ ⦀⦀ | | 21 |
| lime | || | 2 |
| horse chestnut | ⦀⦀ ⦀⦀ |||| | 14 |

The most common type of tree is an oak.

The least common type of tree is a lime.

Work with a partner. You will need **a dice**.

In each question, copy the table. You need one copy between you.

One person rolls the dice.
The other person makes a tally mark for each score in the table.

Change over after every ten rolls.

1  Copy this table. Roll the dice 50 times altogether. Record the score in the table.

| Score | Tally | Frequency |
|-------|-------|-----------|
| 1 |  |  |
| 2 |  |  |
| 3 |  |  |
| 4 |  |  |
| 5 |  |  |
| 6 |  |  |

   a  Which was your most frequent score?

   b  Which score came up the least number of times?

2  Copy this table. Roll the dice 50 times altogether. Record the score in the table.

| Score | Tally | Frequency |
|-------|-------|-----------|
| odd |  |  |
| even |  |  |

Which score did you get more often, **odd** or **even**?

3  Copy this table. Roll the dice 50 times altogether. Record the score in the table.

| Score | Tally | Frequency |
|-------|-------|-----------|
| less than 4 |  |  |
| 4 or more |  |  |

   a  Which score did you get more often, **less than 4** or **4 or more**?

   b  What did you expect would happen? Explain why.

## Extension problem

**4** Design your own dice experiment.

Make a tally chart. Carry out your experiment 50 times. Write about the results.

## Points to remember

⊙ In a tally chart each mark stands for one item.

⊙ The tally marks are grouped in fives.

⊙ The total for the tally is the **frequency**.

## 2 Bar charts

This lesson will help you to draw and interpret bar charts.

## Exercise 2

A **bar chart** helps you to display data. In a bar chart:

◉ all the bars are the same width;

◉ both the vertical and horizontal axes have labels;

◉ there is a gap between the bars;

◉ the bars can be drawn horizontally or vertically.

## Example

This **frequency table** and **bar chart** show how many Year 7 pupils had a school lunch.

| Day | Number of lunches |
|-----|-------------------|
| Monday | 40 |
| Tuesday | 71 |
| Wednesday | 60 |
| Thursday | 55 |
| Friday | 78 |

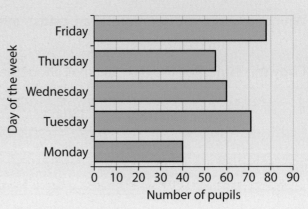

More pupils had a school lunch on Friday than on any other day.

Fewer pupils had a school lunch on Monday.

You will need a ruler, sharp pencil and squared paper.

1 Mrs Chang runs a café.

This table shows the number of ice creams that Mrs Chang sells in a day.

| Flavour | Number sold |
|---------|-------------|
| vanilla | 35 |
| peach | 30 |
| cherry | 5 |
| lemon | 15 |
| lime | 25 |

a Draw a bar chart to show this data.

Make vertical bars 1 cm wide with 1 cm gaps between them.

Number the vertical axis in 5s from 0 to 40.

b Write two sentences about what the bar chart shows.

2 This bar chart shows how many sandwiches Mrs Chang sells in a week.

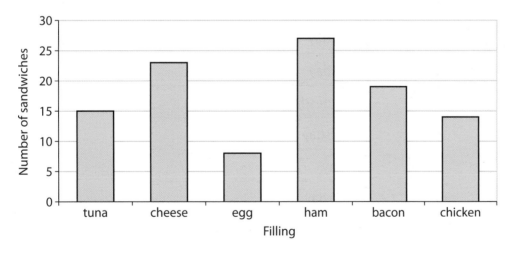

a Write two sentences about what the bar chart shows.

b What would Mrs Chang use this information for?

c Mrs Chang wants to sell only four sandwich fillings.

Which fillings should she choose? Explain why.

**3** This bar chart shows how many customers visited Mrs Chang's café in a week.

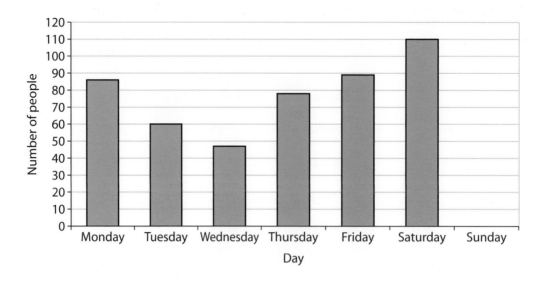

**a** Write two sentences about what the bar chart shows.

**b** What can you say about the café on Sunday?

**c** What could Mrs Chang use this information for?

**4** This table shows how much profit a different café made in one week.

| Day | Profit (£) |
|-----------|------------|
| Monday | 200 |
| Tuesday | 350 |
| Wednesday | 490 |
| Thursday | 310 |
| Friday | 380 |
| Saturday | 550 |
| Sunday | 220 |

**a** Draw a bar chart to show this data.

Make vertical bars 1 cm wide with a gap of 1 cm between them.

Number the vertical axis in 100s from 0 to 600. Space the numbers 2 cm apart.

**b** On which day did the café make the most profit?

**c** On which day did the café make the least profit?

**d** How much more profit did the café make on Saturday than on Monday?

## Extension problem

**5**  These two graphs show how many people went to a swimming pool in a year.

One graph is for the winter months and one for the summer months.

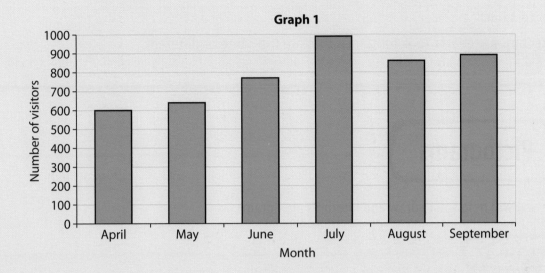

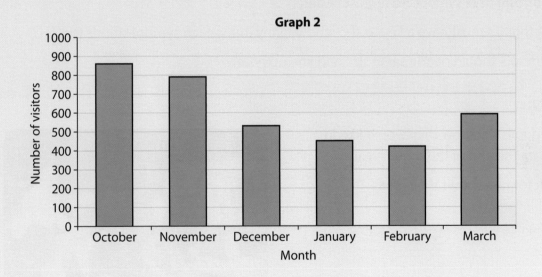

**a**  Which graph is for the summer months?

**b**  Write a sentence to say what the summer graph shows.

**c**  Write a sentence to say what the winter graph shows.

**d**  Did more people go swimming in April or October?

**e**  Which month of the year was the most popular for swimming?

**f**  Which month of the year was the least popular for swimming?

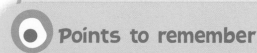
⦿ A **bar chart** helps you to compare data. Important things to look for are:
  – the tallest bar;
  – the shortest bar.

⦿ When you compare charts, look for things that are the same or different.

## 3 Pictograms

This lesson will help you to draw and interpret pictograms.

### Exercise 3

A **pictogram** uses symbols to represent data.

The pictogram must have a key to show how many items each symbol stands for.

The symbols should be the same size and line up neatly.

### Example

Some pupils said how they would like to celebrate the end of the school year.

This pictogram shows their ideas.

| Event trip | ☺ ☺ |
|---|---|
| Disco | ☺ ☺ ( |
| Sports event | ☺ |
| BBQ | ☺ ☺ ☺ ( |

Key: ☺ stands for 2 people

The most popular choice was a BBQ.
It was chosen by 7 pupils.

The second most popular choice was a disco.
Five people wanted a disco.

1 This table shows how many pupils in a year group were late for school in a week.

| Day | Number of pupils |
|---|---|
| Monday | 9 |
| Tuesday | 6 |
| Wednesday | 4 |
| Thursday | 4 |
| Friday | 10 |

a Draw a pictogram to show this data.
  Choose a symbol to stand for 2 pupils.

b On which day were the most pupils late?

c How many more pupils were late on Friday than on Tuesday?

2 Will is sorting out his family's DVDs.
The table shows the number of DVDs he has of each type of film.

| Type | Frequency |
|---|---|
| comedy | 6 |
| cartoon | 8 |
| western | 1 |
| science fiction | 5 |
| war | 3 |
| drama | 8 |
| adventure | 11 |

a Draw a pictogram to show this data.
  Choose a symbol to stand for 2 films.

b Write two sentences about what the pictogram shows.

c How many films do Will's family have altogether?

3 This pictogram shows the number of books borrowed from a library.

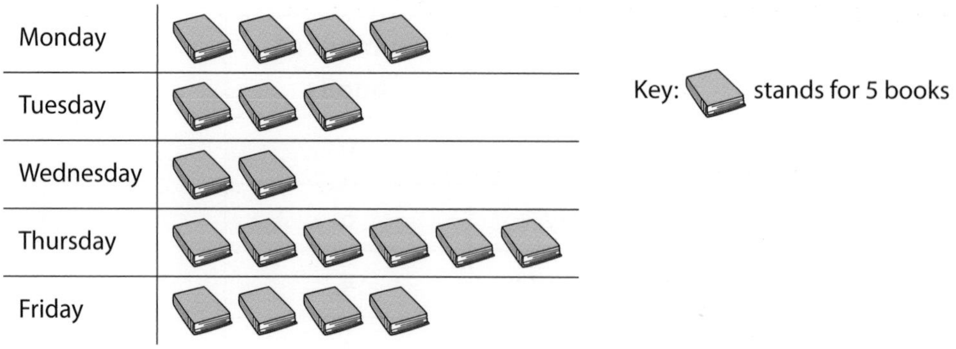

| | |
|---|---|
| Monday | 📕 📕 📕 📕 |
| Tuesday | 📕 📕 📕 |
| Wednesday | 📕 📕 |
| Thursday | 📕 📕 📕 📕 📕 📕 |
| Friday | 📕 📕 📕 📕 |

Key: 📕 stands for 5 books

a How many books were borrowed on Thursday?

b How many more books were borrowed on Tuesday than on Wednesday?

4 This pictogram shows the favourite pastimes of the pupils in Kate's class.

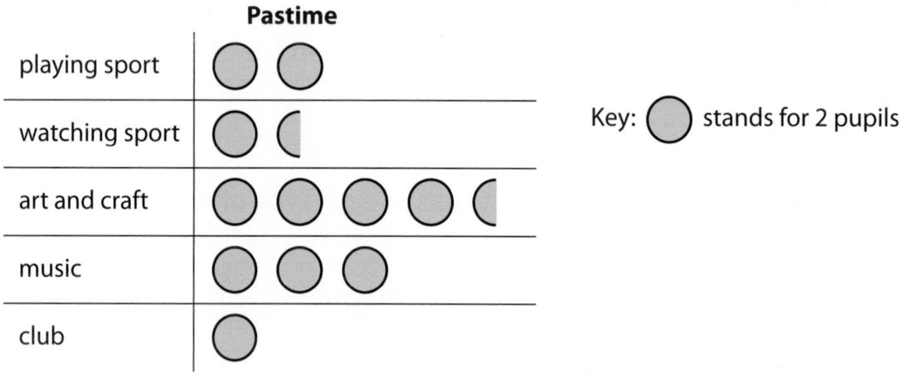

**Pastime**

| | |
|---|---|
| playing sport | ◯ ◯ |
| watching sport | ◯ ◖ |
| art and craft | ◯ ◯ ◯ ◯ ◖ |
| music | ◯ ◯ ◯ |
| club | ◯ |

Key: ◯ stands for 2 pupils

This pictogram shows the favourite pastimes of the pupils in Jamal's class:

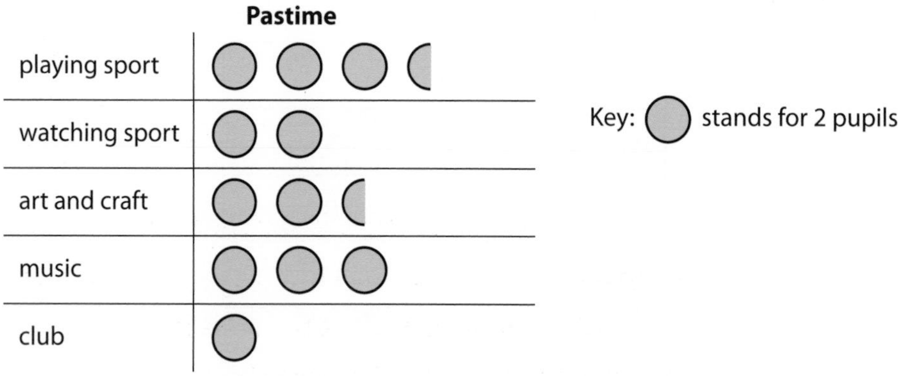

**Pastime**

| | |
|---|---|
| playing sport | ◯ ◯ ◯ ◖ |
| watching sport | ◯ ◯ |
| art and craft | ◯ ◯ ◖ |
| music | ◯ ◯ ◯ |
| club | ◯ |

Key: ◯ stands for 2 pupils

a Write a sentence about the favourite pastimes of Kate's class.

b Write a sentence about the favourite pastimes of Jamal's class.

c Write one thing that is the same about the two classes.

d Write one thing that is different about the two classes.

## Extension problem

 **5** This pictogram shows the points scored by the Blue team on sports day.

**Event**

| sprint | ✳ ✳ |
| run | ✳ ✳ ✳ ⊣ |
| throw | ✳ ✳ |
| long jump | ✳ ✳ ✳ |
| high jump | ✳ ✳ |

Key: ✳ stands for 10 points

This pictogram shows the points scored by the Red team on sports day.

**Event**

| sprint | ✳ |
| run | ✳ ✳ ✳ |
| throw | ✳ ✳ |
| long jump | ✳ ✳ ✳ ⊣ |
| high jump | ✳ ✳ ✳ |

Key: ✳ stands for 10 points

a  Which team was better at jumping?

b  The two teams got the same number of points in one event. Which event?

c  Which team got the most points?

> ### ⊙ Points to remember
>
> ⊙ You can use a **pictogram** to represent data.
> ⊙ A **key** should show how many items each symbol stands for.
> ⊙ A symbol can represent more than one item.
> ⊙ The symbols should be the same size.
> ⊙ The symbols should line up neatly.

## 4 Carroll diagrams

This lesson will help you to use Carroll diagrams.

### Did you know that...?

Carroll diagrams were invented by **Lewis Carroll**, who wrote *Alice in Wonderland*. The Mad Hatter (in the picture) was one of the people Alice met.

Lewis Carroll's real name was **Charles Dodgson**. He was tall, with curly brown hair and blue eyes. He married his cousin Frances and had 11 children.

Charles also taught maths at Oxford University.

A **Carroll diagram** is a special kind of table.

It is used for sorting data into groups.

Every item must have a place in the Carroll diagram.

### Examples

In this Carroll diagram the names of some animals are sorted by whether or not the first letter is 'A'.

| begins with A | does not begin with A |
|---|---|
| antelope  ape | goat  bear  cow |

In this Carroll diagram, the names of the animals are sorted by:

◉ whether or not the first letter is an A;

and:

◉ whether or not the word has 3 letters.

| | begins with A | does not begin with A |
|---|---|---|
| **has 3 letters** | ape | cow |
| **does not have 3 letters** | antelope | goat  bear |

① These shapes are lettered from A to J.

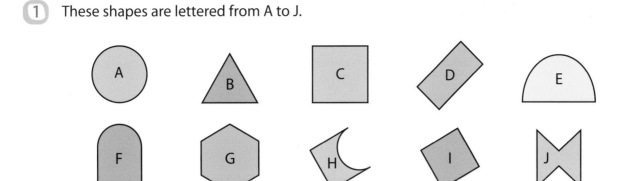

**a** Draw this Carroll diagram.

| blue | not blue |
|---|---|
|  |  |

Write the letters for shapes A to J in the correct places on your diagram.

**b** Draw this Carroll diagram.

| all straight sides | not all straight lines |
|---|---|
|  |  |

Write the letters for shapes A to J in the correct places on your diagram.

**c** Now draw this Carroll diagram.

|  | all straight sides | not all straight lines |
|---|---|---|
| blue |  |  |
| not blue |  |  |

Write the letters for shapes A to J in the correct places on your diagram.

**2** **a** Copy this Carroll diagram.

| odd | not odd |
|-----|---------|
|     |         |

**b** Write these numbers in the correct places on your diagram.

1, 2, 3, 4, 5, 6, 7, 8, 9, 10

**c** Are there more odd or even numbers on your diagram?

**Extension problem**

 **a** Copy this Carroll diagram.

|         | multiple of 3 | not a multiple of 3 |
|---------|---------------|---------------------|
| **odd**     |               |                     |
| **not odd** |               |                     |

Write these numbers in the correct places on your diagram.

5, 6, 7, 8, 9, 10, 11, 12, 13, 14, 15, 16, 17, 18, 19, 20

**b** How many of the numbers are odd multiples of 3?

 **Points to remember**

⊙ A **Carroll diagram** is useful for sorting information.

⊙ All the data must go into one of the boxes in the diagram.

## 5 Venn diagrams

This lesson will help you to use Venn diagrams.

### Exercise 5

A **Venn diagram** is another way to show data in a diagram.

**Example**

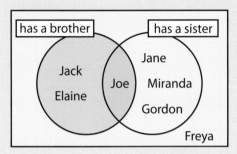

Joe, Jack and Elaine have brothers.

Joe, Jane, Miranda and Gordon have sisters.

Freya has no brothers or sisters.

Joe has a brother and a sister.

1. A group of 6 friends sorted themselves into these sets.

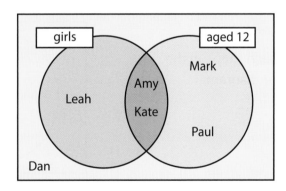

a  How many of the friends are aged 12?

b  Which of the friends are girls aged 12?

c  Who is not a girl and not aged 12?

2. Draw this Venn diagram.

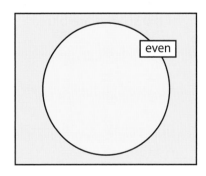

Write each of these numbers in the correct place on your diagram.

5,  6,  7,  8,  9,  10,  11,  12,  13,  14

**3** These shapes are lettered from A to J.

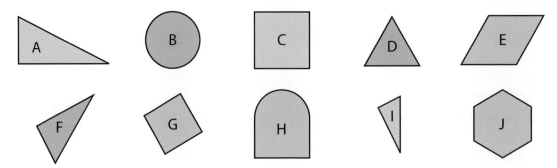

**a** Draw this Venn diagram.

Write the letter for each shape in the correct place on your diagram.

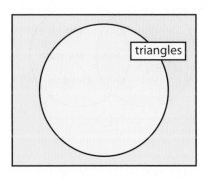

**b** Draw this Venn diagram.

Write the letter for each shape in the correct place on your diagram.

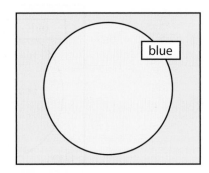

**c** Now draw this Venn diagram.

Write the letter for each shape in the correct place on your Venn diagram.

**d** How many of the shapes are blue triangles?

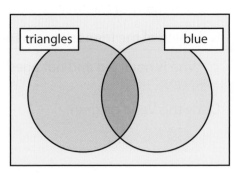

④ Draw this Venn diagram.

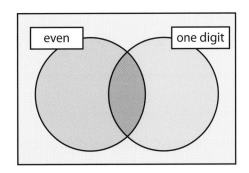

Write each of these numbers in the correct place on your diagram.

1,  2,  3,  4,  11,  12,  13,  14,  21,  22,  23,  24

## Extension problem

⑤ Five pupils sorted themselves into these sets.

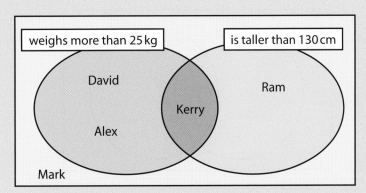

Copy and complete this Carroll diagram to show the same information.

|  | is taller than 130 cm | is **not** taller than 130 cm |
|---|---|---|
| **weighs more than 25 kg** |  |  |
| **does not weigh more than 25 kg** |  |  |

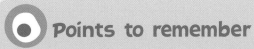  **Points to remember**

⊙ A **Venn diagram** is useful for sorting information.

⊙ Data can go inside or outside the circles depending on its properties.

# How well are you doing?

**Can you:**

● draw and use tally charts, pictograms, bar charts, and Venn and Carroll diagrams?

**1** *2000 level 3*

Copy the Venn diagram.

Write each of these numbers in its correct place on the diagram.

40     8     15

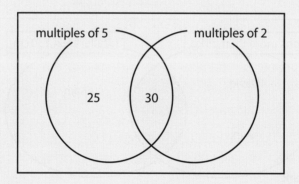

**2** *1998 KS2 level 3*

The table shows the number of shirts in a shop.

|  | white | not white |
|---|---|---|
| cotton | 27 | 56 |
| not cotton | 74 | 90 |

a   How many shirts are white?

b   How many shirts are there altogether?

*2002 level 3*

Tom does a survey of children's favourite breakfast cereals.

a These are the results for Class 6.

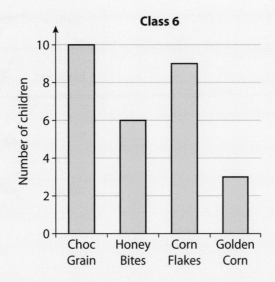

How many more children in Class 6 prefer Choc Grain than Golden Corn?

b These are the results for Class 5.

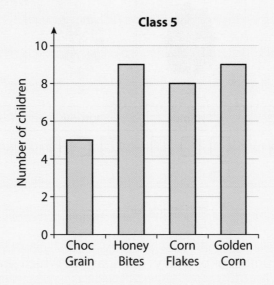

How many children in both classes like Honey Bites best?

**4** *2005 KS1 level 3*

Jane made a tally chart.

How many more gulls than blackbirds did she see?

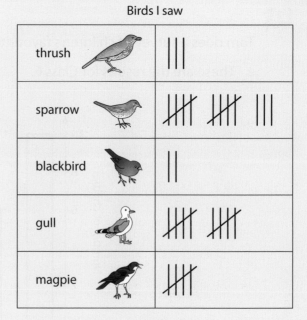

Birds I saw

| | | |
|---|---|---|
| thrush | | III |
| sparrow | | IIII IIII III |
| blackbird | | II |
| gull | | IIII IIII |
| magpie | | IIII |

**5** *2003 KS1 level 3*

Some children made a pictogram.

Seasons our birthdays are in

| spring | summer | autumn | winter |
|---|---|---|---|

☐ stands for → 4 children

**a** There is an even number of birthdays in 2 seasons. Which seasons are they?

**b** How many children have a birthday in the summer?

# Money and decimals

**This unit will help you to:**

- find totals and give change using coins and notes;
- read and write money in pounds and pence;
- change pounds to pence, and vice versa;
- solve money problems, with and without a calculator;
- understand decimals to two places.

## 1 Coins and notes

 **Did you know that...?**

Before 1971, money in the UK was pounds, shillings and pence. Some people call this 'old money'.

There were 12 pence in a **shilling**, and 20 shillings in a pound.

The **ha'penny** was half a penny.
The **farthing** was quarter of a penny.

One of the first ever bicycles was called a **penny farthing**. It had a big front wheel and a much smaller back wheel.

This lesson will help you to find totals and give change using coins and notes.

## Exercise 1

1. How much is this altogether?

**2** How much is this altogether?

**3** What is the smallest number of coins you need to pay these exactly?

Which coins are they?

| | | | | |
|---|---|---|---|---|
| **a** 23p | **b** 68p | **c** 17p | **d** 43p | **e** 88p |
| **f** £1.06 | **g** £1.27 | **h** £5 | **i** £3.25 | **j** £4.91 |

**4** The corner shop sells these.

Mints 42p

Chews 16p

Fruit gums 37p

Lemon fizzer 6p

Choc bar 53p

Pear drops 24p

Jellos 19p

Find the change from £1 when you buy these.

**a** Pear drops

**b** Mints

**c** Chews

**d** Fruit gums

**e** a Choc bar

**f** Jellos and Mints

**g** Pear drops and Fruit gums

**h** Chews and a Choc bar

**i** two Mints and one Lemon fizzer

**j** two Lemon fizzers and one Jellos

**5** Play **Money bags** with a partner.
You need a dice.

### Rules

- Each player should draw a purse like this.
- Take turns.
- Roll the dice. Choose a space in your purse.
  Work out your score. For example, if you roll 4
  and choose the 2p space you win four 2p coins.
  Write 8p in the space.
- Carry on taking turns until all the spaces are full.
- Now work out the total amount in each purse.
  The winner is the player with the greatest total amount.

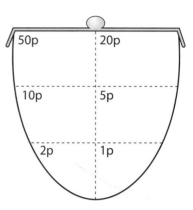

### Extension problem

**6** A packet of toffees costs 20p.

You can pay for it exactly using one 20p coin.

Investigate other ways of paying 20p exactly using 2 coins, 3 coins, 4 coins, …

Keep going up to using 15 coins.

 **Points to remember**

- To find the total value of several coins, group the coins. Start with the coins with the biggest value.
- To find change from £1, count up to the next multiple of 10p, and then on to 100p.

## 2 Pounds and pence

 **Did you know that…?**

In the Second World War, each person was allowed meat worth one shilling and sixpence per week.

Metal for coins was in such short supply that a sixpence note was issued in Jersey.

The design for the sixpence note cleverly showed a V for Victory when it was folded.

This lesson will help you to:
- read and write money in pounds and pence;
- change pounds to pence, and vice versa;
- solve problems involving money calculations without a calculator.

Exercise 2

When you add or subtract pounds and pence, make sure that you line up the pence.

**Example**

£2.87 − 54p = £2.87 − £0.54

```
    £
    2.67
−   0.54
    2.13
```

① Write in pence.

| | | | | |
|---|---|---|---|---|
| a £4.34 | b £15.27 | c £3.05 | d £2.50 | e £0.43 |
| f £0.75 | g £0.08 | h £0.30 | i £0.01 | j £40.00 |

② Write in pounds.

| | | | | |
|---|---|---|---|---|
| a 526p | b 9673p | c 402p | d 650p | e 82p |
| f 46p | g 5p | h 20p | i 1p | j 300p |

③ Work these out **without a calculator**. Show your working.

| | | | |
|---|---|---|---|
| a £2.56 + £2.35 | b £3.74 + £0.28 | c £5.48 + 23p | d £6.51 + 63p |
| e £3.67 − £2.20 | f £3.81 − £0.56 | g £1.63 − 24p | h £4.15 − 68p |

④ Imagine you have two £1 coins, two 10p coins and two 2p coins.

a What amounts can you make using any two of the coins?
Write all your answers in pounds.

b What amounts can you make using any three of the coins?
Write all your answers in pounds.

**5** You can buy these cards at the paper shop.

**a** Rob buys two different cards.

What is the most he can pay?

What is the least he can pay?

**b** Jess has £2. She buys one card.

What is the most change she can get?

What is the least change she can get?

**c** Joe has £3. He buys two identical cards.

What is the most change he can get?

What is the least change he can get?

**d** Ismat buys three different cards.

She pays £2.60 altogether.

Which three cards does she buy?

## Extension problem

**6** Simon has two £2.80 stamps and two £3.25 stamps.
He posts a parcel using one or more of his stamps.

Investigate the possible cost of posting the parcel.

 **Points to remember**

⊙ There are 100 pence in £1.

⊙ £4.67 means 4 pounds and 67 pence.

⊙ The two ways to write 35 pence are 35p or £0.35.

⊙ To change pounds to pence, write the digits without a point.

⊙ To change pence to pounds, make the last two digits the pence.

⊙ To add or subtract pounds and pence, write them in columns.
Line up the points under each other.

# 3 Money problems

This lesson will help you to use a calculator to solve money problems.

## Exercise 3

To enter 56p in a calculator, decide whether you want it in pounds (£) or pence.

To enter it **in pounds** (£), key in: ⓪ ⦁ ⑤ ⑥

To enter it **in pence**, key in: ⑤ ⑥

If the answer to a calculation is in pounds:

| | |
|---|---|
| 4.5 | in the display means £4.50 |
| 13.2 | in the display means £13.20 |
| 0.23 | in the display means 23p |
| 0.04 | in the display means 4p |

You can **use your calculator**.

① You can buy these at the corner café.

pizza £1.35

curry £3.10

sausage and mash £2.65

fish and chips £3.35

pasta £1.95

chips 75p

tomato soup £1.45

sandwich 90p

trifle £2.50

apple 55p

water 45p

salad 85p

What do you pay for these?

**a** a curry and chips

**b** fish and chips and a salad

**c** tomato soup and a pizza

**d** sausage and mash, trifle and water

**e** 2 sandwiches and an apple

**f** 3 pastas and 2 salads

**2** What is the difference in the price of these?

**a** a curry, and pasta

**b** fish and chips, and tomato soup

**3** What change do you get from £10 if you buy these?

**a** 2 curries

**b** 3 pastas

**c** 4 portions of chips

**d** 2 trifles and water

**e** 1 fish and chips and 2 pizzas

**f** 5 sandwiches and 1 apple

**4** All items more than £2.50 are reduced by 62p. What are their new prices?

**5** Which two items can you buy for exactly £6?

**6** Two friends shared equally the cost of a pasta, a curry and a bottle of water. What did each of them pay?

**7** Four friends shared equally the cost of 3 pizzas, 2 chips and a salad. What did each of them pay?

**8** Peter paid £11.70 for several sandwiches. How many did he buy?

**9** **a** How many trifles can you buy for £10? **b** How many apples can you buy for £3?

### Points to remember

- Read problems carefully.
- Change different units to the same unit.
- Decide what sum to do and write it down.
- Decide whether to do the sum in your head, on paper or using a calculator.
- When you use a calculator, think how to interpret the display.
- If you make a mistake using a calculator, press ON and start again.
- Check the answer makes sense.
- Include units in the answer.

## 4 Tenths

This lesson will help you to write tenths as decimals and position tenths on a number line.

## Exercise 4

This number line goes from 6 to 7. It is labelled in tenths.

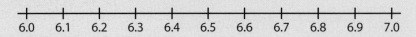

### Example

Write the length of the key.

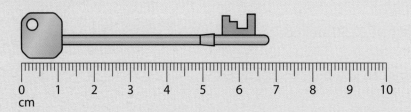

The length of the key is 6 whole centimetres and 8 tenths of a centimetre.

The key is 6.8 cm long.

1. Write the number that each arrow is pointing to.

**a**

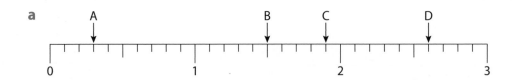

**b**

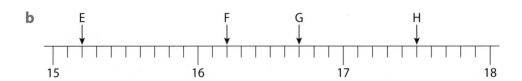

**②** Write in centimetres (cm) the length of each pencil.

**a**

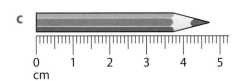

**b**

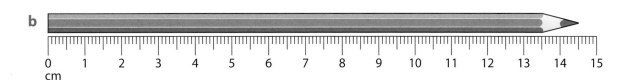

**c**

**d**

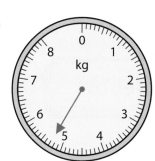

**③** Write in kilograms (kg) the weight on each scale.

**a** **b** **c**

**④** Write these as decimals.

**a** $\frac{1}{10}$ **b** $\frac{3}{10}$ **c** $4\frac{7}{10}$ **d** $6\frac{4}{10}$ **e** $\frac{5}{10}$ **f** $35\frac{9}{10}$

**⑤** Write these as fractions.

**a** 8.4 **b** 6.9 **c** 10.3 **d** 1.7 **e** 0.5 **f** 0.2

**⑥** What are these numbers?

**a** one tenth more than 4.3 **b** four tenths less than 9.5

**c** five tenths more than 2.7 **d** three tenths less than 5.1

## Extension problem

 Write the next three numbers in each sequence.

  **a** 0.1, 0.2, 0.3, ..., ..., ...

  **b** 1.6, 1.7, 1.8, ..., ..., ...

  **c** 3.5, 3.6, 3.7, ..., ..., ...

  **d** 2.4, 3.4, 4.4, ..., ..., ...

  **e** 3.5, 4.0, 4.5, ..., ..., ...

## ◉ Points to remember

- 0.1 means one tenth or $\frac{1}{10}$.
- 0.5 means five tenths or $\frac{5}{10}$, which is the same as $\frac{1}{2}$.
- 3.7 means 3 ones and 7 tenths. You can write 3.7 as $3 + 0.7$, or $3 + \frac{7}{10}$.
- The decimal point separates the whole number from the part less than 1.

## 5 Tenths and hundredths

 **Did you know that...?**

Our money is a **decimal currency**.

We write amounts in pounds (£) in the same way as we write decimals with two places.

  £1.43 is the same as 143p

  98p is the same as £0.98

  8p is the same as £0.08

This lesson will help you to write tenths and hundredths as decimals.

## Exercise 5

Look at the amount £34.72.

The **decimal point** separates the whole number part from the part that is less than £1.

The **3** has a value of **three tens** or **£30**.
The **4** has a value of **four ones** or **£4**.

The first decimal place is for the **tenths**.
The second decimal place is for the **hundredths**.

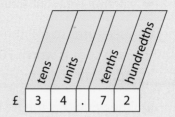

The **7** has a value of **seven tenths** of £1, or **£0.70**.
The **2** has a value of **two hundredths** of £1, or **£0.02**.

① Write the total in pounds (£).

   **a** five £1 coins, six 10p coins and two 1p coins

   **b** fifteen £1 coins, eight 10p coins and one 1p coin

   **c** twenty-seven £1 coins and eight 1p coins

   **d** forty-six £1 coins and seven 10p coins

② Write the value of the **4** in each number.

   **a** 28.43       **b** 413.5       **c** 1.24       **d** 346.7       **e** 0.45

③ Write these as fractions.

   **a** 0.03       **b** 0.04       **c** 0.3       **d** 0.59       **e** 0.4

   **f** 0.95       **g** 0.14       **h** 0.05       **i** 0.6       **j** 0.02

④ Write as decimals.

   **a** $\frac{3}{100}$       **b** $\frac{9}{100}$       **c** $\frac{6}{10}$       **d** $\frac{51}{100}$       **e** $\frac{8}{100}$

   **f** $\frac{29}{100}$       **g** $\frac{1}{10}$       **h** $\frac{7}{100}$       **i** $\frac{1}{100}$       **j** $\frac{37}{100}$

⑤ Write the answers.

   **a** 1p more than £8.35       **b** 4p less than £7.27       **c** 5p more than £6.78

   **d** 3p less than £4.81       **e** 2p more than £5.99       **f** 5p less than £7.05

   **g** 3p more than £1.29       **h** 4p less than £8.03       **i** 10p more than 97p

**6** Play **Make £10** with a partner.
You need a dice.

**Rules**

- Each player starts with £9.50 in their bank.

- Take turns to roll the dice.
  Each spot is worth £0.01.
  Add your score to the money in your bank.

- The winner is the first to get £10 in their bank.

**7** Copy and complete each sequence.

a £5.27, £5.28, £5.29, ..., ..., ...

b £1.73, £1.72, £1.71, ..., ..., ...

c £6.00, £6.05, £6.10, ..., ..., ...

d £3.72, £3.82, £3.92, ..., ..., ...

e £8.24, £8.14, £8.04, ..., ..., ...

f £4.06, £4.04, £4.02, ..., ..., ...

## Points to remember

- The decimal point separates the whole number from the part less than 1.
- Each digit in a decimal has a place value.
- The first decimal place is for tenths and the second decimal place is for hundredths.

# How well are you doing?

## Decimals and money (no calculator)

**1** *2003 KS2 level 3 [adapted]*

**a** Here is part of a number line.
What number is the arrow pointing to?

**b** Work out the answer to 5.3 + 0.9

**2** *2005 level 3*

Here are the prices of food and drinks in a café.

| FOOD | | DRINKS | |
|------|------|--------|------|
| Pizza | £1.40 | Tea | 65p |
| Burger | 95p | Coffee | 90p |
| Sandwich | £1.20 | Cola | 80p |
| Toast | 90p | Juice | £1.00 |

**a** Sally wants to buy one item of food and one drink.
What is the least amount of money she can pay?

**b** Lee buys one item of food and one drink.
He pays with a £5 note and gets £2.60 change.
What did Lee buy?

**3** *2005 level 3*

**a** Write a number bigger than one thousand but smaller than one thousand one hundred.
Write it in figures not words.

**b** Now write a decimal number that is bigger than zero but smaller than one.

**4** *2006 Progress Test level 3*

Nisha writes:

$$538 + 46 = 585$$

Show why Nisha is wrong.

## Decimals and money (calculator allowed)

**5** *2003 Progress Test level 3*

Alice and Ben each buy a bicycle but they pay in different ways.

| Alice pays £179.99 | Ben pays £8.62 every week for 24 weeks |
|---|---|

Ben pays more than Alice.

How much more?
Show your working.

**6** *2005 level 3*

In a theatre, tickets are three different prices.

| Ticket in seating area A | £19.00 |
|---|---|
| Ticket in seating area B | £29.00 |
| Ticket in seating area C | £39.00 |

**a** How many tickets in area A can you buy with £100?

**b** How many tickets in area B can you buy with £200?

**c** Jo buys two tickets in area C. She pays with two £50 notes.
How much change should she get?

# Measures 2

**This unit will help you to:**

- use am and pm for times before and after midday;
- work out how long it is between two times;
- read a timetable;
- use kilograms, grams, litres and millilitres;
- read scales.

## 1 Clocks and timetables

This lesson will help you to use timetables and read and write time using am and pm.

### Exercise 1

Use **am** to show a time in the morning before 12 noon, or midday.

> **6:15 am is quarter past 6 in the morning**

Use **pm** to show a time in the afternoon or evening, after midday.

> **8:45 pm is quarter to 9 in the evening**

### Example

This timetable shows the times of trains from Barrow-in-Furness to Manchester Airport.

| Barrow-in-Furness | 7:00 am | 9:15 am | 11:15 am | 12:20 pm | 2:20 pm |
|---|---|---|---|---|---|
| Manchester Airport | 9:40 am | 11:40 am | 1:40 pm | 2:40 pm | 4:40 pm |

Helen must be at Manchester Airport by 2:30 pm.

What is the latest train that she can catch?    The train leaving Barrow-in-Furness at 11:15 am.

How long does her journey take?    The journey takes:

1 hour + 1 hour + 25 minutes = 2 hours and 25 minutes.

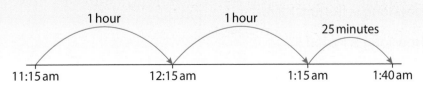

1. Write in digital clock time using am or pm.

   a  Half past 9 in the morning

   b  5 past 3 in the afternoon

   c  20 to 6 in the morning

   d  Quarter to 1 in the afternoon

   e  20 past 8 in the morning

   f  5 to 7 in the afternoon

2. This table shows the high and low tides in Cardiff Bay on 7th August.

   | High tide | 12:20 am |
   |-----------|----------|
   | Low tide  | 6:25 am  |
   | High tide | 12:45 pm |
   | Low tide  | 6:55 pm  |

   a  How long was it between the first high tide and the first low tide?

   b  How long was it between the two high tides?

   c  How long was it between the two low tides?

3. Here are the times for a school day.

   | 9:05 am | Registration/assembly | 12:55 pm | Lunch break |
   |---------|----------------------|----------|-------------|
   | 9:15 am | Locker time | 1:40 pm | Locker time |
   | 9:20 am | Period 1 | 1:45 pm | Period 5 |
   | 10:10 am | Period 2 | 2:35 pm | Period 6 |
   | 11:00 am | Break | 3:25 pm | Locker time |
   | 11:10 am | Locker time | 3:30 pm | Registration |
   | 11:15 am | Period 3 | 3:35 pm | Finish |
   | 12:05 pm | Period 4 | | |

   a  How long does Period 1 last?

   b  How long is the lunch break?

   c  How long is Period 5?

   d  How long is the school day?

**4** **a** Jamie made some marmalade.
He started at 9:50 am.
He finished at 11:25 am.
How long did it take Jamie to make the marmalade?

**b** It is now 11:40 am.
Lunch will be in 45 minutes' time.
What time is lunch?

**c** Jamie took his cake out of the oven at 2:25 pm.
It took 75 minutes to cook.
When did Jamie put the cake in the oven?

**d** Dinner starts at 6:50 pm.
It lasts for $1\frac{1}{4}$ hours.
When does dinner end?

### Extension problem

**5** Here is a timetable for trains from Birmingham New Street to Reading.

| Birmingham New Street | 9:40 am | 10:05 am | 11:05 am | 12:35 pm |
|---|---|---|---|---|
| **Birmingham International** | 9:50 am | 10:15 am | 11:15 am | 12:45 pm |
| **Coventry** | 10:10 am | 10:30 am | 11:30 am | 1:00 pm |
| **Leamington Spa** | 10:25 am | | 11:45 am | 1:15 pm |
| **Oxford** | 11:05 am | 11:20 am | 12:25 pm | 1:55 pm |
| **Reading** | 11:30 am | 11:45 am | 12:50 pm | 2:25 pm |

**a** Which is the fastest train from Birmingham New Street to Reading?

**b** How long does the fastest train take from Birmingham New Street to Reading?

**c** How long does it take the 10:25 am from Leamington Spa to reach Oxford?

 **Points to remember**

⊙ Use **am** to show times in the morning before 12 noon, or midday.

⊙ Use **pm** to show times in the afternoon or evening, after midday.

⊙ To work out a time interval, count on from the start time to the end time.

⊙ You can use a blank time line to help work out time intervals.

# 2 Seconds, minutes, hours, days, weeks

This lesson will help you to remember the number of seconds in a minute, minutes in an hour, hours in a day and days in a week.

## Did you know that...?

Constantine became the Roman Emperor in York, England, in 306 AD.

Constantine made Sunday the first day of the seven-day week in 321 AD.

The Babylonians used a seven-day week about 1000 years before this.

The days were named after six planets and the Sun.

**The Roman Emperor, Constantine**

## Exercise 2

### Example 1

In 1998 Hicham El Guerrouj of Morocco ran 1500 m in 3 minutes and 26 seconds exactly.

How many seconds is that?

There are 60 seconds in a minute

3 minutes = 3 × 60 = 180 seconds

Total time = 180 + 26 = 206 seconds

### Example 2

The Jones family went to New Zealand for 5 weeks and 4 days.
How many days were they in New Zealand?

There are 7 days in a week.

5 weeks is the same as 5 × 7 = 35 days.

The Jones family were in New Zealand for 35 + 4 = 39 days.

## Example 3

A plane leaves London at 6:35 am.
It arrives in Helsinki at 8:55 am.

How long is the flight in:

**a** hours and minutes?

**b** minutes?

**c** seconds?

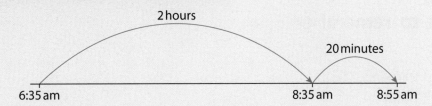

**a** The total journey time is 2 hours and 20 minutes.

**b** There are 60 minutes in 1 hour.
In 2 hours there are 2 × 60 = 120 minutes.
The total journey time is 120 + 20 = 140 minutes.

**c** There are 60 seconds in a minute.
The total journey time is 140 × 60 = 8400 seconds.

You may **use your calculator**.

**1** Change these to days.

    **a** 4 weeks         **b** 9 weeks 3 days         **c** 52 weeks

**2** Change these to hours.

    **a** 3 days         **b** 1 day         **c** $3\frac{1}{2}$ days

    **d** 4 days 6 hours         **e** 1 week         **f** 2 weeks

**3** Change these to minutes.

    **a** 7 hours         **b** 3 hours         **c** $10\frac{1}{2}$ hours

    **d** 24 hours         **e** 2 hours 15 minutes         **f** 9 hours 45 minutes

**4** Change these to seconds.

    **a** 4 minutes         **b** 7 minutes         **c** 5 minutes 8 seconds

    **d** 60 minutes         **e** $12\frac{1}{2}$ minutes         **f** $8\frac{1}{4}$ minutes

## Extension problem

**5** In 1977 Richard Rodriguez rode a roller coaster in America for 104 hours.

This set a new world record.

How many days and hours is this?

---

## ⊙ Points to remember

There are:

- ⊙ 60 seconds in 1 minute;
- ⊙ 60 minutes in 1 hour;
- ⊙ 24 hours in 1 day;
- ⊙ 7 days in 1 week.

## 3 Scales

This lesson will help you read values from different scales.

### Exercise 3

These scales show the weight of some potatoes.

The weight of potatoes is 2 kg.

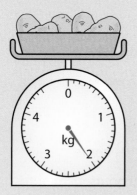

This scale shows the weight of some sugar.

The weight of sugar is 450 g.

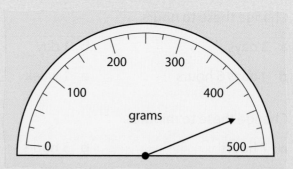

This ruler shows the length of a line. The line is 7 cm long.

1 Write the number marked by:

a arrow A

b arrow B

c arrow C

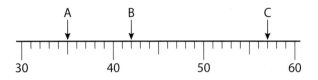

2 Write the number marked by:

a arrow A

b arrow B

c arrow C

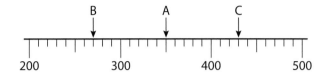

3 Write the reading shown on the ruler's scale by:

a arrow A

b arrow B

c arrow C

d arrow D

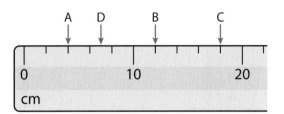

4 Write the number marked by:

a arrow A          b arrow B

c arrow C          d arrow D

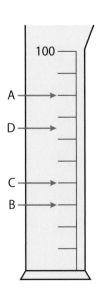

5 Write the number marked by:

a arrow A          b arrow B

c arrow C          d arrow D

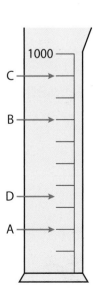

**6** Write the number the arrow is pointing to.

a

b

## Extension problem

**7** Write the reading on each thermometer.

a

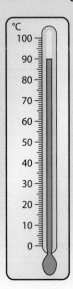

b

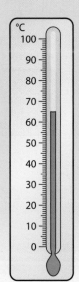

c

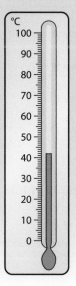

## Points to remember

⊙ Look carefully at a scale to work out the step size.

⊙ The step size on this scale is 5 cm.

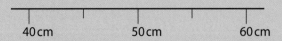

40 cm      50 cm      60 cm

## 4 Mass

**Did you know that...?**

Light things like a wren are measured in **grams**. The short way to write gram is **g**.

Heavy objects like an ocean liner are measured in **kilograms**. The short way to write kilogram is **kg**.

This lesson will help you to estimate and measure the weight of an object.

## Exercise 4

The standard metric units for mass are the **gram** (g) and **kilogram** (kg).

1000 grams = 1 kilogram

1   Write whether you would weigh these objects in kilograms (kg) or grams (g).

**a**  A worm

**b**  An aeroplane

**c**  A stone statue

**d**  An apple

**e**  A box of apples

**f**  A rugby player

**2** Write the readings on these scales. Give the units for each answer.

a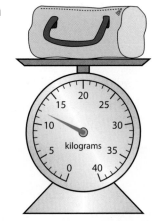

b

c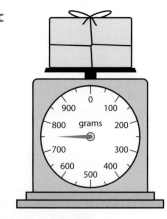

d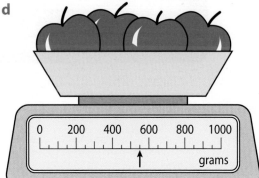

e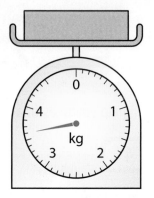

**3** Copy and complete each sentence by choosing one of the weights.

a The weight of an orange is about …… g.

   2 g      20 g      200 g      2000 g

b The weight of a small loaf of bread is about …… g.

   4 g      40 g      400 g      4000 g

c The weight of a paper clip is about …… g.

   5 g      50 g      500 g      5000 g

d The weight of a bag of large potatoes is about …… g.

   3 g      30 g      300 g      3000 g

e The weight of a plum is about …… g.

   8 g      80 g      800 g      8000 g

## Extension problem

 **4** Here is a recipe for a sponge cake.

**a** Each egg weighs 35 g. What do 6 eggs weigh?

**b** What is the total weight of the flour,
butter and sugar?

**c** A bag of flour weighs 630 g before the cake is made.
How much does it weigh afterwards?

> *Sponge cake*
> 6 medium eggs
> 340 g flour
> 340 g butter
> 340 g sugar

 **Points to remember**

⊙ There are 1000 grams in 1 kilogram.

⊙ Lighter objects are measured using grams (g).

⊙ Heavier objects are measured using kilograms (kg).

⊙ 'Kilo' means one thousand.

## 5 Capacity

This lesson will help you to estimate and measure the capacity of a container.

**Did you know that...?**

A large capacity such as the amount of
water in a lake is measured in **litres**.

The short way to write this is **l**.

A small capacity such as the amount of water
in a teaspoon is measured in **millilitres**.

The short way to write this is **ml**.

## Exercise 5

The standard metric units for capacity are the **millilitre** (ml) and **litre** (l).

1000 millilitres = 1 litre

**(1)** Write whether you would measure the capacity of these in millilitres (ml) or litres (l):

**a** Water in a swimming pool

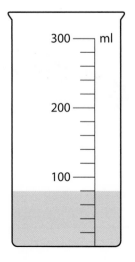

**b** A glass of juice

**c** A kettle

**d** A bottle of medicine

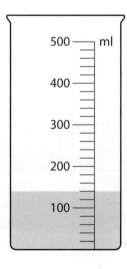

**(2)** These beakers measure in millilitres (ml).
Write the reading on each scale. Give the units for each answer.

**a**

**b**

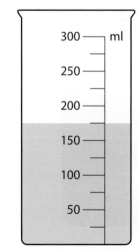

**c**

**3** These jars measure in millilitres (ml).
Write the reading on each scale. Give the units for each answer.

**a**

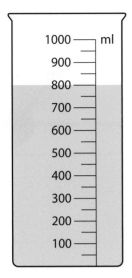

**b**

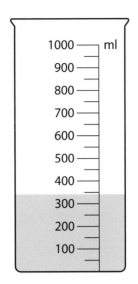

**c**

**4** Copy and complete each sentence by choosing one of the capacities.

**a** The capacity of a bottle of lemonade is about ....... .

2 millilitres      20 millilitres      2 litres      20 litres

**b** The capacity of a kitchen bucket is about ....... .

10 millilitres      100 millilitres      10 litres      100 litres

**c** The capacity of a teaspoon is about ....... .

5 millilitres      50 millilitres      500 millilitres      5 litres

**d** The capacity of an eggcup is about ....... .

5 millilitres      50 millilitres      500 millilitres      5 litres

**e** The capacity of a can of cola is about ....... .

3 millilitres      30 millilitres      300 millilitres      3 litres

(5) A bottle of medicine holds 200 ml of medicine.

    **a** How much medicine is there in half a bottle?

    **b** John takes four 5 ml teaspoons of medicine from a full bottle.
       How much medicine is left in the bottle?

    **c** The correct dose is 10 ml twice a day for 1 week.
       How much medicine is this altogether?

       How long will the bottle last?

(6) Green Fizz is made from green energy drink and soda water.

Recipe for

## 1 glass of Green Fizz

110 ml energy drink
170 ml soda water

Pour green energy drink over ice cubes.

Add soda water and stir well.

    **a** How much Green Fizz does this recipe make altogether?

    **b** How much more soda water than energy drink does the recipe use?

    **c** How much soda water do you need to make 2 glasses of Green Fizz?

## Points to remember

⊙ There are 1000 millilitres in 1 litre.
⊙ Smaller capacities are measured using millilitres (ml).
⊙ Larger capacities are measured using litres (l).
⊙ 'Milli' means one thousandth.

# How well are you doing?

## Can you:

- use am and pm for times before and after midday?
- work out how long it is between two times?
- read a timetable and answer questions about it?
- use kilograms, grams, litres and millilitres and read scales?

**1** *2005 Progress Test level 3*

**10 o'clock in the morning is 10:00 am**

Copy these sentences. Fill in the missing times.

**a** Quarter to 7 in the morning is ..................

**b** Quarter past 7 in the evening is ..................

**2** *1998 level 3*

Look at this bus timetable, from Highbury to Colton.

| Bus timetable: Highbury to Colton | | | | | |
|---|---|---|---|---|---|
| **Highbury** *depart*: | 07:45 | 08:30 | 09:30 | 10:45 | 11:30 |
| **Colton** *arrive*: | 08:30 | 09:15 | 10:15 | 11:30 | 12:15 |

**a** A bus leaves Highbury at 08:30.
What time does it arrive in Colton?
How much time does the bus journey take?

**b** 5 friends are going from Highbury to Colton by bus.
They want to arrive by 10:30.
Which is the latest bus they can catch from Highbury?

**c** Each bus ticket costs £2.20.
How much do the 5 bus tickets cost altogether?

**3** *2006 Progress Test level 3*

Choose from the list of weights below the correct amount to show about how much a cat weighs.

**3 grams   30 kilograms   30 grams   3 kilograms**

**4** *2004 Progress Test level 3*

**a** About how much does a new-born baby weigh?

Choose from:

**0.3 kg   3 kg   30 kg   300 kg**

**b** About how much milk does a baby's bottle hold?

Choose from:

**3 millilitres   300 millilitres   3 litres   300 litres**

**5** *2007 KS1 level 3*

Kemi needs 450 millilitres of water.

How much more water does she needs to put in the jug?

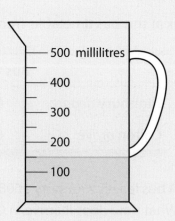

# Number and measures

**This unit will help you to:**

- ⊙ use positive and negative numbers;
- ⊙ read numbers from scales;
- ⊙ count on and back in tenths;
- ⊙ relate tenths to hundredths;
- ⊙ change metres to centimetres and centimetres to millimetres.

## 1 Positive and negative numbers

This lesson will help you to use positive and negative numbers in context.

### Exercise 1

**Negative numbers** have a minus sign in front of them.

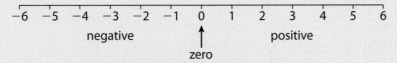

You sometimes see negative numbers on thermometers.

Temperatures below 0°C have a minus sign.

−5°C means 5 degrees below zero.

1  Look at these temperatures.

$$-4°C \quad 2°C \quad 6°C \quad -1°C \quad 5°C$$

a  Which temperatures are below freezing?

b  Which temperature is nearest to 0°C?

c  Write the temperatures in order, coldest first.

2  a  The temperature was 4°C.
It fell by 7 degrees.
What is the new temperature?

b  The temperature was −3°C.
It went up by 6 degrees.
What is the new temperature?

3  At dawn, the temperature was −1°C.
Later the temperature was 3°C.
How many degrees did the temperature go up?

4  The temperature in London was 2°C.
In New York it was −3°C.
How many degrees colder was it in New York?

5  Use a number line to help you.

```
  −6   −5   −4   −3   −2   −1    0    1    2    3    4    5    6
            negative              ↑         positive
                                 zero
```

a  $-3 + 2$          b  $-4 + 7$          c  $-1 + 3$

d  $2 - 5$           e  $4 - 6$           f  $1 - 7$

g  $-5 + 8$          h  $-2 + 2$          i  $6 - 10$

### ◉ Points to remember

⊙  −5 is 'negative 5'.

⊙  −6°C is minus six degrees Celsius. It is six degrees below zero.

⊙  −10°C is a lower temperature than −5°C.

⊙  Include the units when you write a temperature.

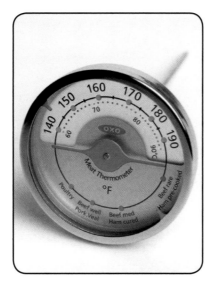

This lesson will help you to read number lines and scales.

## Exercise 2

When you read a scale, work out what the units are and what each interval represents.

### Example 1

The units on this **ruler** are centimetres. Each interval is one tenth of a centimetre, or 1 millimetre.

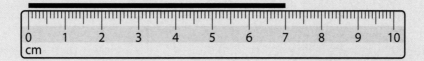

The line is 7 cm long.

### Example 2

This **rain gauge** measures the amount of water in it.

The units are in millilitres (ml).

There are 10 ml of water in the rain gauge.

You need a copy of **N1.7 Resource sheet 2.1** for question 6.

(1) What number is the arrow pointing to?

**a**

**b**

(2) There are some tomatoes on the scales. What is the total weight of the tomatoes?

(3) There is some juice in this jug.

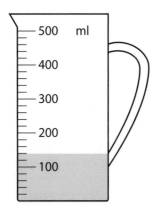

How much more juice is needed to make 500 millilitres of juice?

(4) There is some water in this jar.

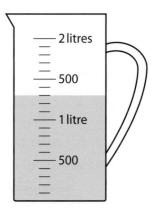

How much more water is needed to make 2 litres?

(5) **a** Tom pours 150 millilitres of water out of this jug.

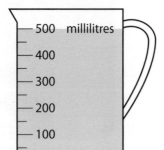

How much water will be left in the jug?

**b** Anna needs 450 millilitres of water in this jug.

How much more water does she need?

**6** Mark the values on the scales on **N1.7 Resource sheet 2.1**.

**7** Estimate how much juice is in each jug.

**a**

500 — ml
400 —
300 —
200 —
100 —

**b**

500 — ml
450 —
400 —
350 —
300 —
250 —
200 —
150 —
100 —
50 —

**c**

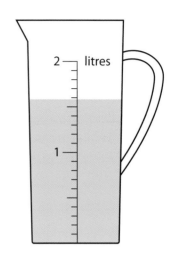

2 — litres

1 —

**Extension problem**

**8** Estimate how much juice is in the jug.

5 — litres
4 —
3 —
2 —
1 —

⊙ **Points to remember**

⊙ A scale can be horizontal or vertical, or straight or curved.
⊙ To read a scale, first work out the step size.
⊙ Work out the values of the marks close to the pointer.
⊙ If the pointer is between two marks, estimate the reading.

## 3 Adding tenths

This lesson will help you to count on in tenths and to use an empty number line to add tenths.

### Did you know that...?

The word **decimal** is from the Latin **decimus**, which means 'tenth'.

The Latin word for ten is **decem**.

The first month in the Roman calendar was March.
**December** means 'the tenth month'.

A shape with ten sides is a **decagon**.

a decagon

## Exercise 3

These number tracks can help you to add tenths by counting on.

| 0 | $\frac{1}{10}$ | $\frac{2}{10}$ | $\frac{3}{10}$ | $\frac{4}{10}$ | $\frac{5}{10}$ | $\frac{6}{10}$ | $\frac{7}{10}$ | $\frac{8}{10}$ | $\frac{9}{10}$ | 1 | $1\frac{1}{10}$ | $1\frac{2}{10}$ | $1\frac{3}{10}$ | $1\frac{4}{10}$ | $1\frac{5}{10}$ | $1\frac{6}{10}$ | $1\frac{7}{10}$ | $1\frac{8}{10}$ | $1\frac{9}{10}$ | 2 |

| 0.0 | 0.1 | 0.2 | 0.3 | 0.4 | 0.5 | 0.6 | 0.7 | 0.8 | 0.9 | 1.0 | 1.1 | 1.2 | 1.3 | 1.4 | 1.5 | 1.6 | 1.7 | 1.8 | 1.9 | 2.0 |

You can also use an empty number line to add tenths by bridging through a whole number.

### Example

5.7 + 0.4

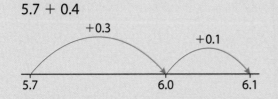

Start with 5.7.
Add three tenths or 0.3 to make 6.
You have one tenth or 0.1 more to add.
Add 0.1 to make 6.1.

**Answer: 6.1**

① Write the number that each arrow is pointing to.

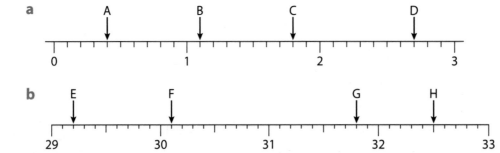

2  Write as decimals:

   **a** $\frac{3}{10}$      **b** $\frac{9}{10}$      **c** $6\frac{1}{10}$      **d** $2\frac{8}{10}$      **e** $17\frac{4}{10}$      **f** $20\frac{5}{10}$

3  Work these out.

   **a** $0.2 + 0.4$      **b** $0.3 + 0.5$      **c** $1.6 + 0.3$      **d** $4.8 + 0.4$

   **e** $1.5 + 0.8$      **f** $3.9 + 0.6$      **g** $2.1 + 0.9$      **h** $5.7 + 0.8$

4  What are these numbers?

   **a** one tenth more than 2.9      **b** six tenths less than 8.6

   **c** five tenths more than 3.8      **d** three tenths less than 7.2

5  Play **Target 5** with a partner. You need a dice.

   ## Rules

   - Each player starts with a score of zero.

   - Take turns to roll the dice.

   - If you roll 5, add 0.5 to your score; if you roll 3, add 0.3 to your score, and so on.

   - If your score reaches 1, 2, 3 or 4 exactly, subtract 1 from your score.

   - The winner is the first player to reach a score of 5 or more.

## Extension problem

6  Write the next three numbers in each sequence.

   **a** 5.1, 5.2, 5.3, …, …, …

   **b** 1.7, 1.8, 1.9, …, …, …

   **c** 6.2, 6.4, 6.6, …, …, …

   **d** 2.4, 2.9, 3.4, …, …, …

## ● Points to remember

- 0.7 and $\frac{7}{10}$ both mean 7 tenths.
- You can add tenths by counting on in tenths.
- Use an empty number line to help add tenths.

## 4 Tenths and hundredths

This lesson will help you to use decimals with two places.

Look at the number 56.83.

The **decimal point** separates the whole number part from the part that is less than 1.

The **5** has a value of **five tens**.
The **6** has a value of **six units or ones**.

The first decimal place is for the **tenths**.
The second decimal place is for the **hundredths**.

The **8** has a value of **eight tenths**.
The **3** has a value of **three hundredths**.

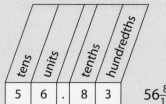

$$56\frac{83}{100}$$

1  Copy and complete.

| units | • | tenths | hundredths | |
|-------|---|--------|------------|---|
| 0 | • | 6 | | $= \frac{6}{10}$ |
| 0 | • | 0 | 5 | $= \frac{5}{100}$ |
| 0 | • | 3 | | |
| 0 | • | 0 | 9 | |
| 2 | • | 7 | | |
| 0 | • | 4 | 8 | |
| 6 | • | 2 | 1 | |
| | | | | $= \frac{3}{100}$ |
| | | | | $= \frac{9}{100}$ |
| | | | | $= \frac{76}{100}$ |
| | | | | $= 5\frac{31}{100}$ |
| | | | | $= 2\frac{11}{100}$ |

2  Write the value of the **7** in each number.

　　a  5.73　　　　　b  71.5　　　　　c  6.27　　　　　d  76.4　　　　　e  0.75

(3) Write as fractions:

a  0.07     b  0.09     c  0.3     d  0.59     e  0.27

f  7.95     g  8.14     h  6.05     i  4.6     j  3.02

(4) Write as decimals:

a  $\frac{6}{100}$     b  $\frac{15}{100}$     c  $\frac{6}{10}$     d  $\frac{51}{100}$     e  $\frac{8}{100}$

f  $6\frac{7}{100}$     g  $9\frac{1}{10}$     h  $7\frac{3}{100}$     i  $17\frac{1}{100}$     j  $25\frac{37}{100}$

(5) Play **Matching pairs** with a partner.
You need a set of cards made from **N1.7 Resource sheet 4.1**.

### Rules

⊙ Spread the cards face down on the table. Shuffle them.

⊙ Take turns.

⊙ Turn over two cards. If they match, you keep them. Have another turn.

⊙ If they don't match, turn them back face down. It is then the other player's turn.

⊙ The winner is the player who wins the most pairs of cards.

(6) Write the answers.

a  one hundredth more than 5.62     b  five hundredths less than 7.87

c  three hundredths more than 1.29     d  four hundredths less than 5.72

---

### ⊙ Points to remember

⊙ The first decimal place is for tenths and the second is for hundredths.

⊙ 1 whole is $\frac{10}{10}$ or $\frac{100}{100}$.

⊙ 0.1 is equivalent to $\frac{1}{10}$ and 0.03 is equivalent to $\frac{3}{100}$.

⊙ 0.56 is equivalent to $\frac{56}{100}$.

# 5 Metres, centimetres and millimetres

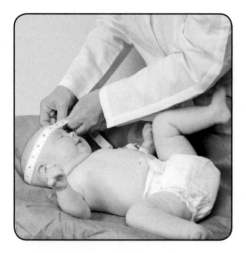
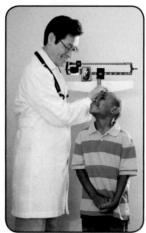

This lesson will help you to use decimals to write metres, centimetres and millimetres.

## Exercise 5

### Metres and centimetres

There are 100 centimetres in 1 metre, so 1 cm is $\frac{1}{100}$ of a metre.

$$1\,cm = 0.01\,m$$
$$5\,cm = 0.05\,m$$
$$64\,cm = 0.64\,m$$
$$283\,cm = 2.83\,m$$

### Centimetres and millimetres

There are 10 millimetres in 1 centimetre, so 1 mm is $\frac{1}{10}$ of a centimetre.

$$1\,mm = 0.1\,cm$$
$$5\,cm = 0.5\,cm$$
$$64\,mm = 6.4\,cm$$

1. Write in metres:

   a  2 cm
   b  58 cm
   c  9 cm
   d  431 cm
   e  975 cm
   f  62 cm
   g  80 cm
   h  1 cm
   i  50 cm
   j  700 cm

2. Write in centimetres:

   a  4 m
   b  3.56 m
   c  0.85 m
   d  0.07 m
   e  0.6 m
   f  8 m
   g  4.22 m
   h  0.15 m
   i  3.06 m
   j  0.9 m

3. Laura is 1.42 metres tall.
   John is 1.35 metres tall.

   Laura is taller than John.
   How many centimetres taller is she?

**4** Some pupils did some long jumps.

**a** The table shows how far some pupils jumped.

Make a table to show how far each pupil jumped in metres.

| Jumps in centimetres | |
|---|---|
| Ruth | 75 cm |
| Sarah | 80 cm |
| Liam | 95 cm |
| Ajit | 103 cm |
| Rupa | 110 cm |
| Harry | 115 cm |

**b** Paul said: 'I jumped 1.5 metres. I jumped further than Harry.'
Give a reason why Paul is correct.

**c** Three pupils put an arrow on a line to show how far they jumped.

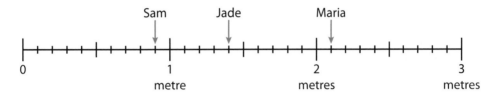

**i** How far did Sam jump in metres?

**ii** How far did Sam jump in centimetres?

**iii** How far did Jade jump in metres?

**iv** How far did Jade jump in centimetres?

**v** How far did Maria jump in metres?

**vi** How far did Maria jump in centimetres?

## ◉ Points to remember

⊙ 1 metre is 100 centimetres.

⊙ 1 centimetre is 10 millimetres.

⊙ You can write 65 cm as 0.65 metres.
465 cm is 4.65 metres.

⊙ You can write 9 mm as 0.9 cm.
29 mm is 2.9 cm.

⊙ When an answer is a measurement, include the units.

# How well are you doing?

## Number and measures (no calculator)

**1** *1995 level 3*

Ali drew a picture to show what there is above and below the sea at Aber.

The anchor is at about −40 m.

a What is at about +10 m?

b What is at about −10 m?

c What is about 30 m higher than the chest?

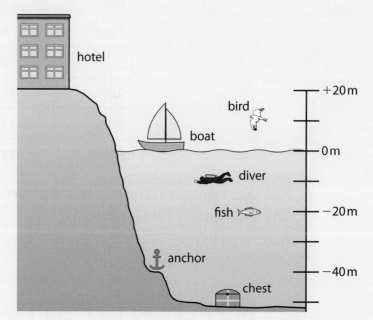

**2** *2003 Progress Test level 3*

a The temperature was −10°C. It went up by 15 degrees.
What is the new temperature?

b Write these temperatures in order, starting with the coldest.

$$-3°C \qquad 0°C \qquad 6°C \qquad -9°C$$

**3** *2006 KS2 level 3*

Here is a baby's drinking cup.

How many millilitres of water are in the cup?

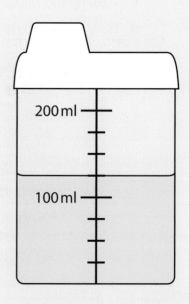

(4) *2005 Progress Test level 3*

a  Steve says there are 1000 centimetres in one metre.
   Is he correct? Write YES or NO.
   Explain your answer.

b  How many millimetres are in one centimetre?

(5) *1997 level 3*

a  What are the two missing numbers: A and B?

Copy and complete this sentence:

The numbers on this line go up in steps of …

b  What are the three missing numbers: C, D and E?

Copy and complete this sentence:

The numbers on this line go up in steps of …

## Number and measures (calculator allowed)

(6) *2006 level 3*

A shop sells birthday cards.
Each card has a code that shows the price.

a  Karen pays for two cards.
   One card has code A on it.
   The other has code C.
   Altogether, how much does Karen pay?

| Code | Price of card |
|------|---------------|
| A    | 95p           |
| B    | £1.25         |
| C    | £1.65         |
| D    | £1.95         |
| E    | £2.35         |

b  Tariq pays for two cards.
   Both cards have code D on them.
   Tariq pays with a £10 note.
   How much change should he get?

c  Greg pays for two cards.
   Altogether he pays £3.60.
   What could the codes on his cards be?
   There are two different answers.
   Write them both.

# More properties of shapes

**This unit will help you to:**

- name shapes and identify their properties;
- make 2D and 3D shapes and patterns;
- know that a whole turn is four right angles or 360°;
- order a set of angles;
- use the eight points of the compass;
- find the position of a point on a grid.

## 1 Properties of polygons

This lesson will help you to sort and organise polygons using their properties.

### Exercise 1

A **polygon** is a 2D shape with straight sides.

Here are some polygons.

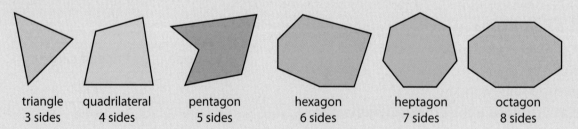

| triangle<br>3 sides | quadrilateral<br>4 sides | pentagon<br>5 sides | hexagon<br>6 sides | heptagon<br>7 sides | octagon<br>8 sides |

A **rectangle** and a **square** are special types of **quadrilateral**.

**Regular** shapes have equal sides and equal angles.

Shapes that are not regular are called **irregular**.

### Example

What properties has this regular hexagon?

It has six sides and six vertices.

It has no right angles and six lines of symmetry.

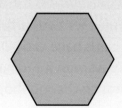

You will need a set of plastic or card polygons to share among a group.

1. Find five polygons with at least one line of symmetry.
   Draw round them. Write their names.

2. Find five polygons with at least one right angle.
   Draw round them. Write their names.

3. Draw a table like this.

| At least one right angle | No right angles |
|---|---|
|  |  |

   In the correct columns, write:

   a the names of four shapes that could have at least one right angle;

   b the names of four shapes that could have no right angles.

4. Write the name of each shape.

   a Holly's shape has four sides and one right angle. What could it be?

   b Nathan's shape has three vertices and no right angles. What could it be?

   c Mia's shape has no lines of symmetry and three sides. What could it be?

   d Tom's shape has four right angles. What could it be?

5. Pick a shape and keep it secret.
   Write two of its properties.

   Show the properties to your partner.
   Can your partner work out which shape you chose?

**Points to remember**

⊙ You can sort shapes using properties such as:
   – number of sides;
   – number of vertices;
   – number of right angles;
   – number of lines of symmetry;
   – whether the shapes are regular or irregular.

# 2 Making 2D shapes and patterns

This lesson will help you to make patterns and shapes with 2D shapes.

## Exercise 2

A repeating pattern with no gaps or overlaps is called a **tessellation.**

These pictures show examples of tessellations.

You can fit shapes together to make new shapes or patterns.

You will need some triangular dotty paper and a set of tessellating shapes.

① You can make only one shape by joining two regular triangles side to side.

The new shape is a quadrilateral.

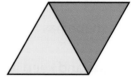

  a Copy the shape above on triangular grid paper. Colour it with one colour.

  b Draw and colour all the shapes you can make with 3 triangles.
     Write the name of each new shape.

  c Draw and colour all the shapes you can make with 4 triangles.
     Write the name of each new shape.

  d Draw and colour all the shapes you can make with 5 triangles.
     Write the name of each new shape.

② Use your set of shapes to make tessellations.
   Draw round the shapes to show the pattern.

  a What tessellating patterns can you make with only triangles?

  b What tessellating patterns can you make using two different shapes?

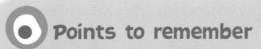

## Points to remember

⊙ A **tessellation** is a repeating pattern of shapes with no gaps or overlaps.

⊙ You can make new shapes by:
   – fitting together shapes with equal sides;
   – cutting across a shape with a straight line.

# 3 Making 3D shapes

This lesson will help you to make shapes and patterns with 3D shapes.

## Exercise 3

You can use cubes to build new 3D shapes.

Each of these shapes is made from 3 cubes.

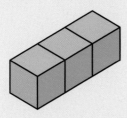 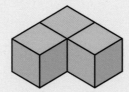 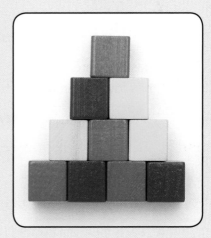

You will need some interlocking cubes.

① There are two different ways to fit 3 identical interlocking cubes together.

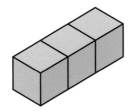 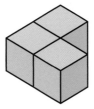

Fit 4 cubes together.

Now fit another 4 cubes together in a different way.

In how many different ways can you fit together 4 cubes?

(2) Look at these drawings. Use interlocking cubes to make them.

a 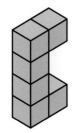　　b 　　c 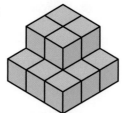　　d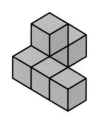

(3) How many cubes have been used to build these shapes?

a 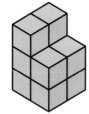　　b 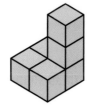　　c 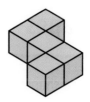　　d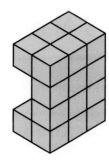

(4) Kirsty is thinking of a 3D shape.

It has a square base.
It has four other faces, which are triangles.

What is the name of Kirsty's shape?

## Extension problem

(5) Write whether these statements are **True** or **False**.

a Each face of a cuboid is a square.

b A cuboid has the same number of edges as a cube.

c A triangular prism has five faces.

d A cone has three faces.

## Points to remember

⊙ You can build 3D shapes by joining other 3D shapes.

⊙ A **prism** has a constant cross-section.

⊙ The triangular faces of a **pyramid** meet at a point.

## 4 Angle

This lesson will help you to know that a right angle is a quarter turn and to order a set of angles.

 **Did you know that...?**

The **ancient Babylonians** may have been the first people to have used 360° to measure a whole turn.

This happened before 300 BC.

They might have used 360° because there are about 360 days in a year.

The Babylonians also counted in 60s.

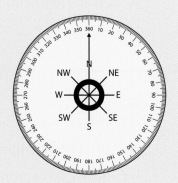

## Exercise 4

Angle is a measure of turn.

There are 360° in a whole turn and 180° in a half turn.

The symbol ° stands for degrees.

### Example

Which of these two angles is smaller?

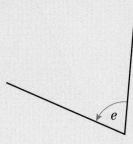

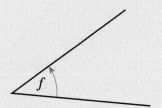

Angle *f* is smaller.

You need a copy of **G1.5 Resource sheet 4.1** between two, scissors and some tracing paper.

1 Work with a partner.

Cut out the angle cards on **G1.5 Resource sheet 4.1**.

Put the angles in a line in order of size, starting with the smallest.
Use the tracing paper to help you find the larger angle.

**2** Play **Angle line** with a partner.

You need the angle cards from **G1.5 Resource sheet 4.1**.

Draw a line 40 cm long on a piece of paper.
Put a mark every 5 cm.

Label the left-hand end of the line 'smallest' and the right-hand end 'largest'.

smallest                                                                largest

## Rules

- Shuffle the angle cards. Put them face down.

- Take turns to turn over the top card and place it on the line.

- Once you have put a card down you can't move it.

- Angles must be placed in order of size, from smallest to largest.

- If you can't put your card down, you miss a go and keep the card.

- The winner is the player with the fewest cards when all the cards have been used.

**3** Trace the shapes.

Then, on each shape, write S in the smallest angle and L in the biggest angle.

a
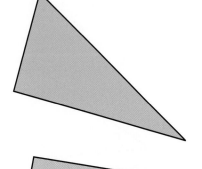

b
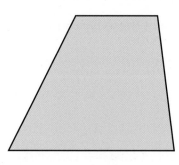

c
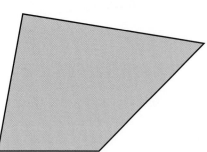

d
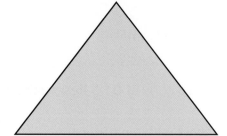

(4) The pointer is pointing to the number 1.

What number is the pointer pointing to after:

a   a quarter turn clockwise?

b   a half turn anticlockwise?

c   a three-quarter turn clockwise?

d   a whole turn anticlockwise?

(5) The pointer is pointing to the number 8.

What number is the pointer pointing to after:

a   an anticlockwise turn through 1 right angle?

b   a clockwise turn through 2 right angles?

c   an anticlockwise turn through 3 right angles?

d   a clockwise turn through 4 right angles?

(6) After a half turn, the hand of a clock is pointing to the number 4.
What number was it pointing to before the turn?

## Extension problem

**7** A whole turn is 360 degrees or four right angles.
A half turn is 180 degrees or 2 right angles.
A quarter turn is 90 degrees or 1 right angle.

Write down a possible number of degrees for an angle that is:

a   between a half turn and a full turn;

b   less than a quarter turn;

c   between a half turn and a quarter turn.

## ◉ Points to remember

- ⊙ Angle is a measure of turn.
- ⊙ Angles are measured in degrees.
- ⊙ The symbol ° stands for degrees.
- ⊙ There are 360° in a whole turn and 180° in a half turn.

## 5 Using the eight compass points

This lesson will help you to use the eight points of the compass to give directions.

### Exercise 5

The four main compass points are **north**, **east**, **south** and **west**.

**North-east** is halfway between north and east.

**South-east** is halfway between south and east.

**North-west** is halfway between north and west.

**South-west** is halfway between south and west.

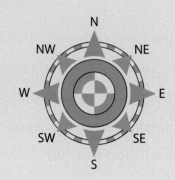

You need plain paper, a ruler, pencil and coloured pencils.

1   This is Jo's treasure map.

    **a**   The first part of the directions
       to find the treasure is:

       Walk 5 paces north-east.

       Finish the directions to Jo's treasure.

    **b**   How many paces in total is the route?

    **c**   What direction is the treasure
       directly from the start point?

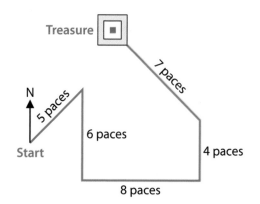

2   Make your own treasure map.
    It can be on an island, at sea, underground, or wherever you like.

    Draw a compass rose to show the eight points of the compass.

    Mark a route on it.
    The route must go north, south, east, west, north-east, south-east, south-west
    or north-west.

    Write out the directions for your route to the treasure.
    Assume 1 cm on your map is roughly 1 pace.

    Swap maps with a friend. Check each other's routes.

**3** Write how many right angles to turn clockwise:

**a** from north-west to north-east

**b** from south-west to north-east

**c** from north-west to south-east

**d** from south-west to south-east

**e** from south-west to north-west

## Extension problem

 Write how many degrees it is to turn clockwise:

**a** from north-west to north-east

**b** from south-west to south-east

### Points to remember

- Compass points are used to give directions.
- The eight main compass points are north, east, south and west, north-east, south-east, south-west and north-west.

## 6 Coordinates

This lesson will help you to use coordinates to describe position on a grid.

### Exercise 6

**Coordinates** tell you where points are on a grid.

Both axes are numbered.
The numbers are on the grid lines, not in the spaces.

The coordinates of the point P are (**4**, **5**).

The first number is always the number of steps across.

The second number is always the number of steps up.

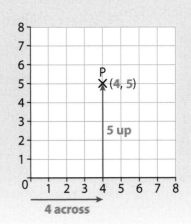

You need squared paper, a ruler and coloured pencils.

① Copy this grid.

Mark these points on the grid with a cross.

Label them with their letter.

A (4, 2)          B (5, 7)

C (5, 4)          D (7, 1)

E (2, 4)          F (0, 7)

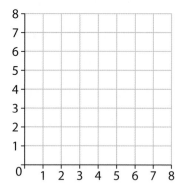

② Points G, H, I, J, K, L, M are marked on the grid.

Write the coordinates of each point.

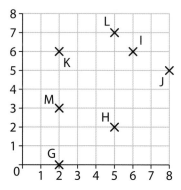

③ Make a copy of the grid you used for question **1**.

**a** Plot these points on the grid.

(6, 6), (4, 2), (7, 8), (5, 4), (3, 0)

What do you notice about the points?

**b** Use a different coloured pencil.
Plot these points on the same grid.

(0, 4), (7, 4), (4, 4), (6, 4), (2, 4)

What type of line do these points make?

**c** Use a different colour pencil.
Plot these points on the same grid.

(2, 8), (2, 7), (2, 3), (2, 6), (2, 7)

What type of line do these points make?

## Extension problem

**4** You need a copy of **G1.5 Resource sheet 6.1**.

Alien spaceships have landed on Earth.

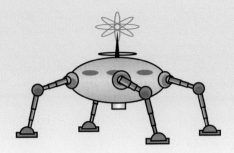

Do the questions on the resource sheet.

 **Points to remember**

- **Coordinates** describe where a point is on a grid.
- Number both axes.
- Label the grid lines not the spaces.
- To plot coordinates, go across first and then up.
- (4, 6) means 4 steps across and 6 steps up.

# How well are you doing?

1  *2007 level 3*

Look at these five shapes.

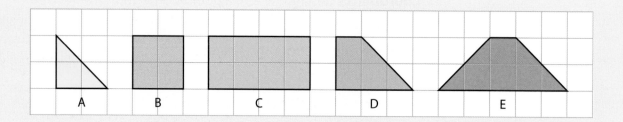

a  Shape A is the only shape with three sides.

Copy and complete these sentences.

Shape ...... is the only shape with no right angles.

Shape ...... is the only shape with no lines of symmetry.

b  Now copy and complete this sentence.

Shape B is the only shape with four ...........................

**2** *2003 KS2 level 3*

Sita had a square.

She cut a triangle of this size off each corner.

What is the name of the shape that is left?

Choose from:

**square    pentagon    hexagon    heptagon    octagon**

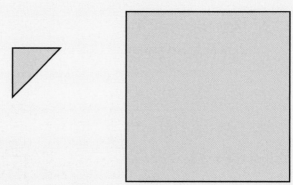

**3** *2006 level 3*

a   Look at this quadrilateral.

Which angle is biggest?

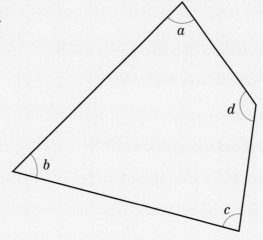

b   Now look at this quadrilateral.

Angle *e* is marked with straight lines.

What does this tell you about the angle?

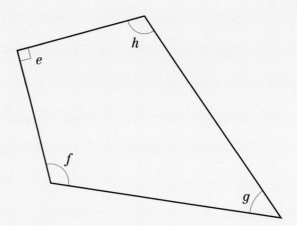

Look at the diagram.

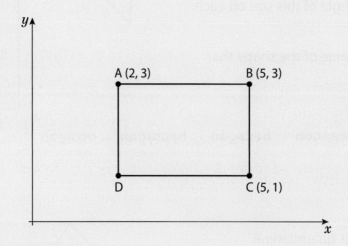

a   The point K is halfway between points B and C.

What are the coordinates of point K?

b   Shape ABCD is a rectangle.

What are the coordinates of point D?

# Multiplying and dividing 2

**This unit will help you to:**

- ⊙ remember times tables;
- ⊙ multiply and divide by 10 or 100;
- ⊙ recognise multiples;
- ⊙ multiply and divide, using a calculator when needed;
- ⊙ find remainders and decide whether to round answers up or down.

## 1 Tables to 10

This lesson will help you to work out and remember tables facts.

### Exercise 1

**The 7 times table**

| × | 1 | 2 | 3 | 4 | 5 | 6 | 7 | 8 | 9 | 10 |
|---|---|---|---|---|---|---|---|---|---|----|
| 1 | | | | | | | 7 | | | |
| 2 | | | | | | | 14 | | | |
| 3 | | | | | | | 21 | | | |
| 4 | | | | | | | 28 | | | |
| 5 | | | | | | | 35 | | | |
| 6 | | | | | | | 42 | | | |
| 7 | 7 | 14 | 21 | 28 | 35 | 42 | 49 | 56 | 63 | 70 |
| 8 | | | | | | | 56 | | | |
| 9 | | | | | | | 63 | | | |
| 10 | | | | | | | 70 | | | |

**10 times** a number **minus** the number is **9 times** a number.

#### Example:

| ten 7s | minus | 7 | equals | nine 7s |
|--------|-------|---|--------|---------|
| $10 \times 7$ | – | 7 | = | $9 \times 7$ |
| 70 | – | 7 | = | 63 |

**The 8 times table**

| × | 1 | 2 | 3 | 4 | 5 | 6 | 7 | 8 | 9 | 10 |
|---|---|---|---|---|---|---|---|---|---|----|
| 1 | | | | | | | | 8 | | |
| 2 | | | | | | | | 16 | | |
| 3 | | | | | | | | 24 | | |
| 4 | | | | | | | | 32 | | |
| 5 | | | | | | | | 40 | | |
| 6 | | | | | | | | 48 | | |
| 7 | | | | | | | | 56 | | |
| 8 | 8 | 16 | 24 | 32 | 40 | 48 | 56 | 64 | 72 | 80 |
| 9 | | | | | | | | 72 | | |
| 10 | | | | | | | | 80 | | |

**10 times** a number **plus** the number is **11 times** a number.

#### Example:

| ten 8s | plus | 8 | equals | eleven 8s |
|--------|------|---|--------|-----------|
| $10 \times 8$ | + | 8 | = | $11 \times 8$ |
| 80 | + | 8 | = | 88 |

Do these **without a calculator**. Show your working.

1. Write the answers.

   **a** 7 × 6      **b** 7 × 9      **c** 7 × 7      **d** 4 × 7      **e** 7 × 8

   **f** 8 × 6      **g** 8 × 9      **h** 8 × 8      **i** 4 × 8      **j** 8 × 7

2. Use two of these numbers each time.

   Copy and complete these.

   **a** ...... × ...... = 56      **b** ...... × ...... = 48      **c** ...... × ...... = 72

   **d** ...... × ...... = 35      **e** ...... × ...... = 45      **f** ...... × ...... = 54

   **g** ...... × ...... = 63      **h** ...... × ...... = 42      **i** ...... × ...... = 40

3. CDs cost £8 and DVDs cost £9.
   What do these cost?

   **a** 6 CDs            **b** 8 DVDs                  **c** 7 CDs and 5 DVDs

   **d** 5 CDs and 7 DVDs      **e** 9 CDs and 9 DVDs      **f** 8 CDs and 6 DVDs

4. Draw two 3 by 3 grids.

   Write the numbers 1 to 9, in any
   order, in one of the grids.
   For example:

   As quickly as you can, write the
   answers for the **9 times table** in
   the right place in the other grid.

   |   |   |   |
   |---|---|---|
   | 5 | 1 | 6 |
   | 2 | 9 | 4 |
   | 7 | 8 | 3 |

   ×9

   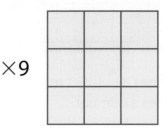

5. Write the answers.

   **a** 56 ÷ 7      **b** 28 ÷ 7      **c** 49 ÷ 7      **d** 63 ÷ 7      **e** 42 ÷ 7

   **f** 48 ÷ 8      **g** 32 ÷ 8      **h** 56 ÷ 8      **i** 72 ÷ 8      **j** 64 ÷ 8

**6** Play this **Seven times table** game with a partner.
You need cards from 0 to 9, and a calculator.

### Rules

- Shuffle the cards. Put them face down.
- The first player turns over a card, multiplies it by 7, and says the answer.
- At the same time, the second player uses the calculator to multiply the card number by 7 and reads out the answer.
- The player who first says the right answer wins the card.
  If it is a draw, put the card back at the bottom of the pile.
- Carry on until all the cards have been won.
- The player who wins the most cards wins the game.

Play again. This time the other player uses the calculator.

> ## Points to remember
>
> - Use facts that you know to work out facts you forget.
> - To multiply a number by 9, multiply it by 10 and subtract the number.
> - To multiply a number by 11, multiply if by 10 and add the number.
> - To multiply by 8, multiply by 4 and double.

## 2 Multiplying by multiples of 10 or 100

This lesson will help you to multiply by numbers like 50 or 400.

### Did you know that...?

The Mayans ruled Mexico up to 1000 AD.

They wrote numbers with dots and dashes.
A dot was 1 and a dash was 5.

They even had a symbol for zero.
It was shaped a bit like a mouth.

| 0 | 1 | 2 | 3 | 4 |
|---|---|---|---|---|
| ⬭ | • | •• | ••• | •••• |
| **5** | **6** | **7** | **8** | **9** |
| — | •⎯ | ••⎯ | •••⎯ | ••••⎯ |

## Exercise 2

| When you: | For example: |
|---|---|
| × **10**, the digits move **1 place to the left**; | 35 × 10 = 350 |
| × **100**, the digits move **2 places to the left**; | 35 × 100 = 3500 |
| ÷ **10**, the digits move **1 place to the right**; | 4800 ÷ 10 = 480 |
| ÷ **100**, the digits move **2 places to the right**; | 4800 ÷ 100 = 48 |

To **multiply a number by 50**:

multiply by 5,
then multiply by 10.

### Example

Work out 8 × 50

8 × 5 = 40 and 40 × 10 = 400

So 8 × 50 = 400

---

Do these **without a calculator**.

① Copy and complete these.

    **a** 32 × 100 = …       **b** 28 × 10 = …       **c** 47 × … = 470

    **d** 50 × 10 = …       **e** 90 × 100 = …       **f** 24 × … = 2400

② Copy and complete these.

    **a** 360 ÷ 10 = …       **b** 4530 ÷ 10 = …       **c** 890 ÷ … = 89

    **d** 2600 ÷ 100 = …       **e** 8000 ÷ 100 = …       **f** 3100 ÷ … = 310

③ Copy and complete these grids.

**a**

| × | 50 | 60 | 70 | 80 |
|---|---|---|---|---|
| 3 | | | | |
| 4 | | | | |
| 5 | | | | |

**b**

| × | 200 | 500 | 300 | 400 |
|---|---|---|---|---|
| 7 | | | | |
| 8 | | | | |
| 9 | | | | |

④ What is the cost of each of these?

    **a** 20 books at £5 each       **b** 30 CDs at £8 each       **c** 50 DVDs at £9 each

    **d** 70 cakes at £3 each       **e** 40 T-shirts at £7 each       **f** 90 pens at £2 each

⑤ Choose a **blue** operation for the first arrow. ×3  ×5  ×6  ×7

Choose a **pink** operation for the second arrow. ×1   ×10   ×100

Copy and complete these.

**a** 9 → ...... → 450

**b** 4 → ...... → 2800

**c** 5 → ...... → 30

**d** 8 → ...... → 240

**e** 6 → ...... → 3600

Now choose a **blue** operation for the first arrow.

Choose **pink** operations for the second and third arrows.

**f** 2 → ...... → ...... → 140

**g** 5 → ...... → ...... → 1500

**h** 9 → ...... → ...... → 2700

**i** 3 → ...... → ...... → 9000

⊙ **Points to remember**

⊙ When a number is:

×10, its digits move 1 place to the left;

×100, its digits move 2 places to the left.

⊙ When a number is:

÷10, the digits move 1 place to the right;

÷100, the digits move 2 places to the right.

⊙ To multiply by 70, multiply by 7, then multiply by 10.

⊙ To multiply by 700, multiply by 7, then multiply by 100.

## 3 Recognising multiples

This lesson will help you to spot multiples.

### Exercise 3

**Multiples of 20** are **20, 40, 60, 80, 10, 120, 140**, …

**Multiples of 50** are **50, 100, 150, 200, 250, 300**, …

**Multiples of 100** are **100, 200, 300, 400, 500, 600**, …

① Play **Whoppers** with a partner.

You need **N1.8 Resource sheet 3.1**, a calculator and two pens in different colours.

**Rules**

◉ Take turns.

◉ Choose one number from each box.

| 4 | 5 | 6 | 7 | 8 | 9 |
|---|---|---|---|---|---|

| 20 | 30 | 60 | 70 | 80 | 90 |
|----|----|----|----|----|----|

| 240 | 320 | 160 | 450 | 270 |
|-----|-----|-----|-----|-----|
| 120 | 400 | 630 | 360 | 100 |
| 80 | 810 | 560 | 720 | 210 |
| 150 | 350 | 640 | 420 | 140 |
| 280 | 480 | 180 | 540 | 300 |

◉ Multiply them to make a number on the grid. Say which board number it is.

◉ Your partner checks with a calculator.

◉ If it's right, cross out the grid number with your pen. Otherwise, miss that turn.

◉ Carry on until all the board numbers are crossed out or the time is up.

◉ The player who crosses out more numbers wins the game.

② Look at these numbers.

300    540    200    450    250    280

a   Which are multiples of 100?

b   Which are multiples of 50?

c   Which are multiples of 20?

**3**　**a** What is the 2nd multiple of 20?　　**b** What is the 3rd multiple of 20?

　　**c** What is the 5th multiple of 20?　　**d** What is the 10th multiple of 20?

**4**　20 is a multiple of several different numbers.
　　Which numbers are they?
　　Write them all.

**5**　Play **Gozinto** with a partner.

　　You need the grid on **N1.8 Resource sheet 3.2**,
　　two dice, a calculator, and two pens in
　　different colours.

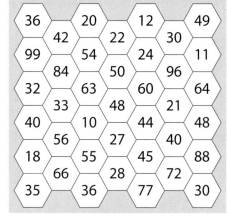

### Rules

- Take turns.

- Roll both dice. Add the numbers to get your score.

- Find a multiple of your score on the grid.
  Say which number it is.

- Your partner checks with a calculator that the grid
  number divides exactly by the score.

- If so, cross out the multiple with your pen. Otherwise, miss that turn.

- The winner is the first to cross out four numbers in a straight line in any direction.

### Extension problem

**6**　60 is a multiple of several different numbers.
　　Which numbers are they?
　　Write them all.

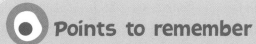

## Points to remember

- A **multiple** of a number divides exactly by the number.
- Multiples of 10 end in 0; multiples of 100 end in 00.
- Multiples of 5 end in 5 or 0; multiples of 50 end in 50 or 00.

# 4 Multiplication

This lesson will help you to multiply in your head, using a written method or using a calculator.

## Exercise 4

A **product** is the answer when you multiply numbers.

You can multiply numbers using a grid.

### Example

Calculate 157 × 3.

157 = 100 + 50 + 7

| × | 100 | 50 | 7 |
|---|-----|-----|-----|
| **3** | 300 | 150 | 21 |

300 + 150 + 21 = 471

**Answer: 471**

Split 157 into **100 + 50 + 7**.

Make a grid.
Multiply 100 by 3 to get 300.
Multiply 50 by 3 to get 150.
Multiply 7 by 3 to get 21.

Add 300, 150 and 21.

Do questions 1 to 5 **without a calculator**. Show your working.

**1** Draw a grid like this.

Write the numbers from 2 to 9 in any order along the top and side.

| × | 5 | 8 | 6 | 2 |
|---|---|---|---|---|
| 3 | | | | |
| 7 | | | | |
| 9 | | | | |
| 4 | | | | |

Fill in the grid as quickly as you can. Have a race with your partner.

| × | 5 | 8 | 6 | 2 |
|---|---|---|---|---|
| 3 | 15 | | | |
| 7 | | | | |
| 9 | | | | |
| 4 | | | | |

**2** Work these out.

**a** 43 × 5

**b** 36 × 4

**c** 57 × 3

**d** 138 × 2

**e** 246 × 3

**f** 369 × 5

③ Find the cost of these.

a Three packets of Trail Mix at 37p each.

b Four jars of peanuts at 64p each.

c Five packets of sunflower seed at 46p each.

d Six tins of cashews at 58p each.

e Two tins of biscuits at 83p each.

④ Use only the digits **3**, **4** and **7**.
Make calculations like this.

You can get six different answers. Find them all.

⑤ Look at these numbers.

|   150   |   350   |   2   |   250   |   4   |

a Which two numbers have a product of 500?

b Which two numbers have a product of 600?

⑥ **Use your calculator**. Show your working.

a There are 52 weeks in a year.
How many weeks in 6 months?
How many weeks in 3 months?

b How many hours do you spend in bed each week?
How many hours will you spend in bed in the next 3 months?

c How many hours of TV do you watch each week?
How many hours of TV will you watch in the next 6 months?

## Extension problem

 **7** **a** Copy and complete the table on the right.

**b** Work out the difference between each product and the next one.

What did you notice?
Describe the pattern.

$1 \times 2 = \ldots$
$2 \times 3 = \ldots$
$3 \times 4 = \ldots$
$4 \times 5 = \ldots$
$5 \times 6 = \ldots$
$6 \times 7 = \ldots$
$7 \times 8 = \ldots$
$8 \times 9 = \ldots$
$9 \times 10 = \ldots$

**c** Use the pattern to copy and complete these.

$10 \times 11 = \ldots$
$11 \times 12 = \ldots$
$12 \times 13 = \ldots$
$13 \times 14 = \ldots$

##  Points to remember

- Read word problems carefully.
- Decide what calculation to do and write it down.
- Estimate the answer before you work it out.
- Use a grid to multiply, or a calculator to multiply bigger numbers.
- Show your working.
- Check that the answer is about the right size.
- Include any units in the answer.

## 5 Division

### Did you know that...?

The **division sign** ÷ has a special name. It is called an *obelus*.

The Swiss mathematician **Johann Rahn** used it first in 1659 in an algebra book.

Before that ÷ was often used to mean 'minus'.

It must have been very confusing!

This lesson will help you to divide numbers using a written method or using a calculator.

### Example

Calculate 136 ÷ 4. This means work out how many 4s make 136.

First, estimate the answer. Work out:

$4 \times 10 = 40$
$4 \times 20 = 80$
**$4 \times 30 = 120$**
**$4 \times 40 = 160$**

**120** and **160** trap the number 136.

This tells you that the answer to 136 ÷ 4 is between **30** and **40**.

```
4) 624
  −120      4 × 30     First take away 30 fours, or 120.
    16                 This leaves 16.
    16      4 × 4      Then take away 4 fours, or 16.
     0      4 × 34     There is 0 left.
                       Altogether, you have taken away 34 fours.
```

**Answer:** 136 ÷ 4 = 34

Do questions 1 and 2 **without a calculator**.

**1** Work these out.

    **a** 96 ÷ 3           **b** 135 ÷ 5           **c** 72 ÷ 4

    **d** 138 ÷ 3          **e** 156 ÷ 4        **f** 185 ÷ 5

**2** Look at each problem. Do you multiply or divide?

    **a** A tin of paint costs £2.39.
       Find the cost of 16 tins of paint.

    **b** A machine fills 108 paint tins in one hour.
       How many tins does it fill in 12 hours?

    **c** A tin of paint holds 3 litres.
       Rose needs 40 litres of paint.
       How many tins of paint should she buy?

**d** A concert ticket costs £1.60.
A school collects £488 from
sales of concert tickets.
How many tickets have been sold?

**e** There are 34 rows of seats in a hall.
Each row has 42 seats.
How many seats are there?

**f** Concert programmes cost 85p.
How many programmes can you
buy for £10?

**g** A box contains 24 chocolates.
How many boxes must you buy
to get 300 chocolates?

**h** Sienna paid £19.25 for boxes of toffees.
Each box cost £1.75.
How many boxes did she buy?

**i** A box contains 18 chocolates.
Ed bought 6 boxes.
How many chocolates did he get?

**j** Max works for 38 hours.
He is paid £241.30.
How much does he earn in an hour?

**k** Zara is paid £7.85 an hour.
She works for 14 hours.
How much does she get paid?

**l** Sanjay earns £8.20 an hour.
He is paid £164.
How many hours did he work?

**3** Look again at the problems in question **2**.
**Use your calculator** to work out the answers.

## Extension problem

Do this question **without using your calculator**.

 **4** A coach can carry 52 people.

3000 football fans go to London.
Work out how many coaches they need.
Show your working

> ## ⦿ Points to remember
>
> ⦿ Read word problems carefully.
>
> ⦿ Decide what calculation to do and write it down.
>
> ⦿ Estimate the answer before you work it out.
>
> ⦿ Use 'chunking' to divide, or a calculator for bigger numbers.
>
> ⦿ Show your working.
>
> ⦿ Check that the answer is about the right size.
>
> ⦿ If necessary, decide whether to round the answer up or down.
>
> ⦿ Include any units in the answer.

# How well are you doing?

Can you:

◉ remember times tables?

◉ multiply and divide, using a calculator when needed?

◉ find remainders and decide whether to round answers up or down?

## Multiplying and dividing (no calculator)

**1** *1999 KS2 level 3*

Rob has some number cards.

**a** He holds up a card. He says:
'If I multiply the number on this card by 5,
the answer is 35.'
What is the number on the card?

**b** He holds up a different card. He says:
'If I divide the number on this card by 6,
the answer is 4.'
What is the number on the card?

**2** *2001 level 3*

Look at this multiplication table.

| ×  | 11  | 12  | 13  | 14  | 15  |
|----|-----|-----|-----|-----|-----|
| 21 | 231 | 252 | 273 | 294 | 315 |
| 22 | 242 | 264 | 286 | 308 | 330 |
| 23 | 253 | 276 | 299 | 322 | 345 |
| 24 | 264 | 288 | 312 | 336 | 360 |
| 25 | 275 | 300 | 325 | 350 | 375 |

Use the table to copy and complete these calculations.

**a** 24 × 13 = …

**b** 15 × … = 300

**c** 288 ÷ 24 = …

**d** … × … = 264

**3** *2002 level 3*

   **a** Multiply 56 by 3.

   **b** Divide 130 by 5.

# Multiplying and dividing (calculator allowed)

**4** *2004 Progress Test level 3*

It is 228 miles from New York to Washington.

To change miles to kilometres use this rule:

$$\text{miles} \longrightarrow \boxed{\times\ 1.6} \longrightarrow \text{kilometres}$$

How many kilometres is it from New York to Washington?

**5** *2004 Progress Test level 3*

What is the missing number?

$$\boxed{\phantom{00}} \times\ 57\ =\ 1938$$

**6** *2001 KS2 level 3*

Plants are sold in trays of 20.

   **a** Ivana buys 7 trays of plants.
      How many plants is this?

   **b** David wants 240 plants.
      How many trays does he need to buy?

# Functional skills 4

## Eating out

**This group activity will help you to:**

- ⊙ work out how to solve a practical problem;
- ⊙ choose the maths to do to solve it;
- ⊙ communicate your solution.

Work in a group of four.

Your group will act as four friends: Amy, Dean, Emma and Carl.
Decide who will play each part.

Write the values of the notes and coins on the right on slips of paper,
or you could make slips for the £5 and £10 notes and use plastic coins.

## Background

The four friends have a meal in a café.

This is what each meal costs.

| Amy | Dean | Emma | Carl |
|---|---|---|---|
| £7.37 | £10.12 | £8.36 | £9.68 |

Each friend has to pay the right amount for their own meal.

## Paying a bill for a meal

The diagram shows the cash they have with them.

| Amy | Dean | Emma | Carl |
|-----|------|------|------|
| £5 | £5 | £10 | £1 |
| £1  £1 | £5 | £1 | 50p  50p |
| £1  £1 | £5 | 50p  50p | 20p |
| 20p  20p | £1  £1 | 10p  5p | 5p |
| 20p  10p | 5p  2p | 2p | |
| 2p  2p | 1p | 1p | |

Carl does not have enough money to pay cash for his meal.

Amy, Dean and Emma say they will pay Carl for their meals.

Then Carl can pay for all four meals by cheque.

No one has the right money.

They give each other change so that Carl can collect the right amount.

Find a way to record all your exchanges.

Be ready to discuss your solution with other groups.

# Graphs and charts 3

## This unit will help you to:

⊙ draw and interpret data in lists and tables, frequency tables, tally charts, bar charts, pictograms and Venn and Carroll diagrams.

## 1 Lists and tables

This lesson will help you to interpret data in lists and tables.

### Exercise 1

### Did you know that...?

In 2012, the Olympic Games will be held in London.

The Olympic logo has five rings.

The colours of the rings are from the flags of every country in the world.

This **table** shows where the Summer Olympic Games have been held since 1964.

| Year | Place |
| --- | --- |
| 1964 | Tokyo, Japan |
| 1968 | Mexico City, Mexico |
| 1972 | Munich, Germany |
| 1976 | Montreal, Canada |
| 1980 | Moscow, Russia |
| 1984 | Los Angeles, USA |

| Year | Place |
| --- | --- |
| 1988 | Seoul, South Korea |
| 1992 | Barcelona, Spain |
| 1996 | Atlanta, USA |
| 2000 | Sydney, Australia |
| 2004 | Athens, Greece |
| 2008 | Beijing, China |

In 2012, the Summer Olympic Games will be held in London.

The data in this exercise is from www.olympic.org.

1   This table shows where the Winter Olympic Games have been held since 1964.

| Year | Place |
|------|-------|
| 1964 | Innsbruck, Austria |
| 1968 | Grenoble, France |
| 1972 | Sapporo, Japan |
| 1976 | Innsbruck, Austria |
| 1980 | New York, USA |
| 1984 | Sarajevo, Yugoslavia |

| Year | Place |
|------|-------|
| 1988 | Calgary, Canada |
| 1992 | Albertville, France |
| 1994 | Lillehammer, Norway |
| 1998 | Nagano, Japan |
| 2002 | Salt Lake City, USA |
| 2006 | Turin, Italy |

a   Where were the Winter Games in 1972?

b   When were the Winter Games in Lillehammer?

c   How many times have the Winter Games been in Austria?

d   When did Canada last hold the Olympic Games?

e   The Winter Games are usually every four years. When did this change?

2   This table shows the gold, silver and bronze medals won by Ian Thorpe, an Australian swimmer.

a   How many Olympic Games did Ian Thorpe compete in?

b   How many medals did he win altogether?

c   How many medals did he win in 2004?

d   In what year did he win a gold medal for the 200 m freestyle?

| Year | Events | Medal |
|------|--------|-------|
| 2000 | 200 m freestyle | ○ |
| 2000 | 400 m freestyle | ○ |
| 2000 | 4 × 100 m freestyle relay | ○ |
| 2000 | 4 × 100 m medley relay | ○ |
| 2000 | 4 × 200 m freestyle relay | ○ |
| 2004 | 100 m freestyle | ○ |
| 2004 | 200 m freestyle | ○ |
| 2004 | 400 m freestyle | ○ |
| 2004 | 4 × 200 m freestyle relay | ○ |

**3** This table shows the Olympic records for the women's high jump.

| Name | Country | Distance (m) | Year | Place |
|---|---|---|---|---|
| Yelena Slesarenko | Russia | 2.06 | 2004 | Athens |
| Stefka Kostadinova | Bulgaria | 2.05 | 1996 | Atlanta |
| Louise Ritter | USA | 2.03 | 1988 | Seoul |
| Ulrike Meyfarth | West Germany | 2.02 | 1984 | Los Angeles |
| Sara Simeoni | Italy | 1.97 | 1980 | Moscow |

**a** Which country is Yelena Slesarenko from?

**b** When did Louise Ritter gain the Olympic record?

**c** How far did Sara Simeoni jump?

**d** For how many years did Louise Ritter hold the Olympic record?

## Extension problem

**4** This table shows some more Olympic gold medallists.

| Name | Country | Birth year | Gold | Silver | Bronze |
|---|---|---|---|---|---|
| Andre Agassi | USA | 1970 | 1 | 0 | 0 |
| Ian Thorpe | Australia | 1982 | 5 | 3 | 1 |
| Carl Lewis | USA | 1961 | 9 | 1 | 0 |
| Steve Redgrave | Great Britain | 1962 | 5 | 0 | 1 |
| Katarina Witt | Germany | 1965 | 2 | 0 | 0 |
| Jane Torvill | Great Britain | 1957 | 1 | 0 | 1 |

**a** Who won the most gold medals?    **b** Who won the most medals altogether?

**c** Who was born in 1962?    **d** Who is 5 years younger than Katarina Witt?

 **Points to remember**

- **Lists and tables** show data in a variety of ways. They help you to:
  - compare information;
  - look for things that are the same or different;
  - look for patterns.

This lesson will help you to use lists and tables in different situations.

### Exercise 2

 **Did you know that...?**

A normal year has 365 days. A leap year is 366 days.

There is one extra day in February. It has 29 days instead of the normal 28 days.

**Example**

Five friends went out for lunch. This table shows what they ordered.

| Name | Main course | Extras | Drink |
| --- | --- | --- | --- |
| Afzal | fish | jacket potato | orange juice |
| Courtney | pasta | salad | lemonade |
| Bradley | fish | chips | lemonade |
| Halima | fish | salad | apple juice |
| Teresa | chicken | chips | cola |

How many of the friends had salad? 2

Who had apple juice? Halima

Who had the same to drink as Courtney? Bradley

1 This is a calendar for February 2007.

a How many days were there in February 2007?

b What date was the third Friday in February 2007?

c On what day of the week was:

i Valentine's Day, February 14th?

ii March 1st?

iii 31 January?

| February 2007 | | | | | | |
| --- | --- | --- | --- | --- | --- | --- |
| Mo | Tu | We | Th | Fr | Sa | Su |
|  |  |  | 1 | 2 | 3 | 4 |
| 5 | 6 | 7 | 8 | 9 | 10 | 11 |
| 12 | 13 | 14 | 15 | 16 | 17 | 18 |
| 19 | 20 | 21 | 22 | 23 | 24 | 25 |
| 26 | 27 | 28 |  |  |  |  |

**2** Here are the opening times at Bourne Castle.

### Bourne Castle Opening Times

| | July 1st to August 31st | September 1st to June 30th |
|---|---|---|
| Monday to Friday | 10 am – 7 pm | closed |
| Saturday and Sunday | 9 am – 8 pm | 1 pm – 5 pm |

**a** At what time does the castle close on Wednesday August 17th?

**b** For which months is the castle open seven days a week?

**c** On Saturday April 9th Hannah goes into the castle at 3 pm.
She stays until closing time.
For how many hours does she stay in the castle?

**3** These are the opening times at a swimming pool.

| | Opening times | | |
|---|---|---|---|
| | am | | pm |
| Monday | Pool closed | | |
| Tuesday | | | |
| Wednesday | 10:30 | to | 5:30 |
| Thursday | 10:30 | to | 8:30 |
| Friday | 10:30 | to | 9:00 |
| Saturday | 8:00 | to | 6:00 |
| Sunday | 7:00 | to | 4:00 |

**a** How many hours is the pool open on a Sunday?

**b** Which day has the latest closing time?

**c** Josh arrives at the pool at 5:20 pm on Saturday.
How many minutes is it before the pool closes?

**4** The Brimble Clothing Company charges for postage and packing.

| Cost of contents | Postage and packing cost | |
| --- | --- | --- |
| | UK | Europe |
| Up to £9.99 | £3.00 | £4.25 |
| £10 to £19.99 | £3.80 | £6.25 |
| £20 to £29.99 | £4.60 | £8.25 |
| £30 to £39.99 | £5.40 | £10.25 |

What does it cost to send:

**a** a parcel worth £20 to Europe?    **b** a parcel worth £20 to the UK?

**c** a parcel worth £35 to the UK?    **d** a parcel worth £17 to Europe?

## Extension problem

**5** This table shows some information about vegetables.

| Vegetable | Number of days to grow to full size | Size | Colour |
| --- | --- | --- | --- |
| cucumber | 55–65 | 15–20 cm long | dark green |
| peas | 55–85 | 8 cm long pods | bright green |
| pepper | 60–90 | 3–8 cm long | red, purple, yellow, green |
| tomato | 70–90 | depends on type | red |
| turnip | 45–70 | 5–8 cm across | white |

**a** Which vegetable comes in the largest number of colours?

**b** Which vegetables are green?

**c** Which vegetable takes the longest to grow?

**d** Which vegetable grows most quickly?

**e** Which is the smallest vegetable?

 **Points to remember**

- A calendar is a kind of table.
- Tables can show different kinds of information for different purposes.

## 3 Bar charts

This lesson will help you to represent and interpret data as a bar chart.

### Exercise 3

These **bar charts** show how many letters were delivered to a house, a small office and a big factory in a week.

They all have different **scales**.

This graph is for **the house**.

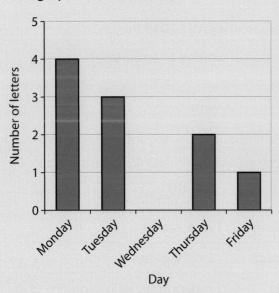

This graph is for the **small office**.

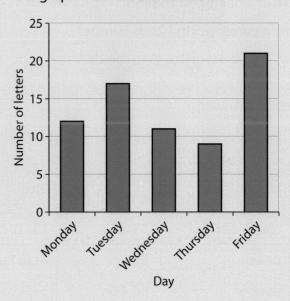

This graph is for the **big factory**.

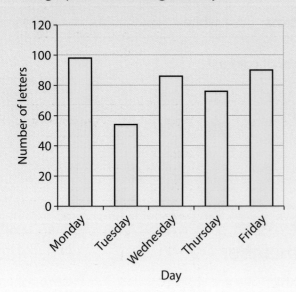

The graph for the house has a vertical scale numbered in 1s.

The graph for the small office has a vertical scale numbered in 5s.

The graph for the big factory has a vertical scale numbered in 20s.

You will need squared paper.

1. Habib counted some trees he saw in West Wood.

   a How many ash trees were there?

   b How many oak trees were there?

   c How many elm trees were there?

   d How many oak and ash trees were there altogether?

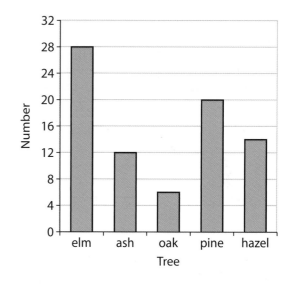

2. Emily counted the birds she saw in West Wood.

   a Use squared paper.

   Draw a bar chart to show this data.

   Space the bars at 1 cm intervals.
   Use a vertical scale numbered in 4s.

   b Which bird was the most common?

   c Which bird was the least common?

   d How many more robins were there than jays?

| Bird | Number seen |
| --- | --- |
| blue tit | 12 |
| thrush | 24 |
| wren | 8 |
| robin | 22 |
| pigeon | 2 |
| jay | 16 |

③ Luke made a bar chart to show the plants he saw in West Wood.

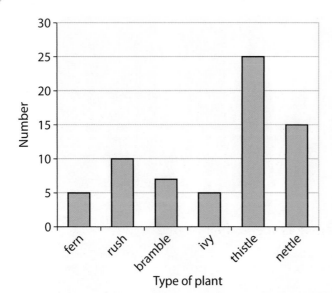

| Plant | Number seen |
|---|---|
| fern | |
| rush | |
| bramble | 7 |
| ivy | |
| thistle | |
| nettle | |

Copy and complete the table to show the data from the bar chart.

④ Sara made a table to show the wildlife she saw in West Wood.

| Wildlife | Number seen |
|---|---|
| newt | 4 |
| deer | 2 |
| squirrel | 16 |
| rabbit | 8 |
| slug | 6 |
| toad | 3 |

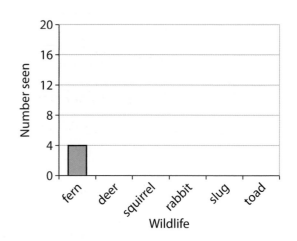

**a** Use squared paper.

Copy and complete the bar chart to show the information in the table.

**b** Write two sentences about what the bar chart shows.

# 4 Interpreting pictograms

This lesson will help you to interpret data in pictograms.

## Exercise 4

A **pictogram** uses symbols to represent data.

A pictogram has a **key** to show how many items each symbol stands for.

### Example

This pictogram shows how some teenagers spend their pocket money.

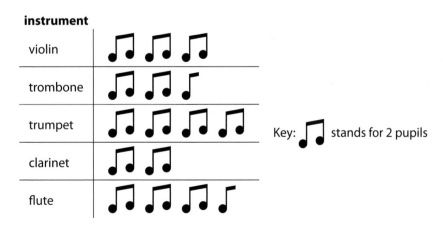

10 of the teenagers spend their pocket money on their hobbies.

7 of the teenagers save their money.

1   This pictogram shows what instrument some pupils would like to learn.

**instrument**

| violin | ♫ ♫ ♫ |
| trombone | ♫ ♫ ♪ |
| trumpet | ♫ ♫ ♫ ♫ |
| clarinet | ♫ ♫ |
| flute | ♫ ♫ ♫ ♪ |

Key: ♫ stands for 2 pupils

**a**  How many pupils want to play the flute?

**b**  Which instrument is most popular?

**c**  How many pupils altogether want to play the violin or the clarinet?

2 40 pupils were asked which outdoor sport they liked best.

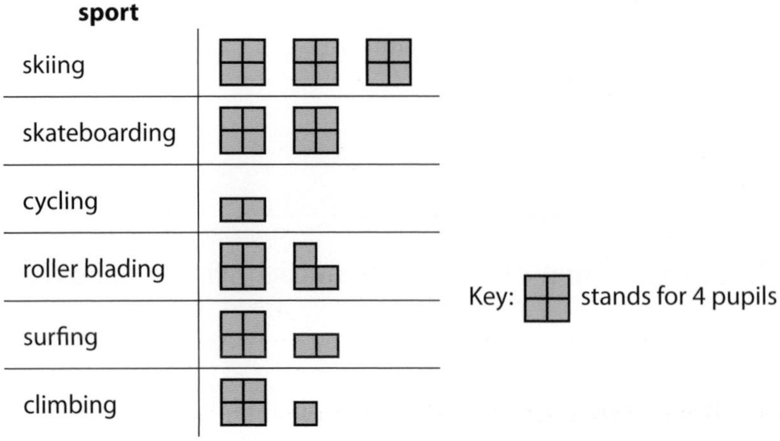

**sport**

Key: ⊞ stands for 4 pupils

Copy and complete these sentences about the pictogram.

a 6 pupils liked ........... .

b Most pupils liked .......... .

c Fewest pupils liked ......... .

3 Some pupils took part in a survey about their favourite kind of TV programme.

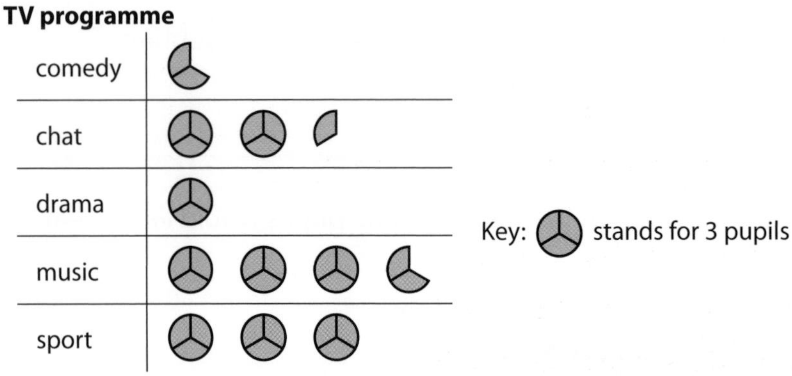

**TV programme**

Key: ◍ stands for 3 pupils

a Which sort of programme did 7 pupils choose?

b Copy and complete these sentences.

The pictogram shows that most pupils liked .......... .

Fewest pupils liked ........... programmes.

c How many pupils altogether took part in the survey?

**4** This pictogram shows the number of letters a school got in one week.

**Number of letters**

| | |
|---|---|
| Monday | ✉ ✉ |
| Tuesday | ✉ ✉ ◻ |
| Wednesday | ✉ ✉ ✉ ▯ |
| Thursday | ✉ ✉ ✉ |
| Friday | ✉ ✉ ✉ ✉ ✉ |

Key: ✉ stands for 20 letters

a How many letters did the school get on Monday?

b How many letters did the school get on Tuesday?

c How many letters did the school get on Wednesday?

d How many more letters did the school get on Friday than on Thursday?

**5** The pictogram shows the number of drinks sold in one day at a café.

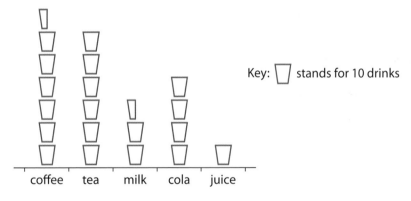

Key: ▯ stands for 10 drinks

coffee   tea   milk   cola   juice

a Which drink was the least popular?

b Which drink was the most popular?

c How many drinks of tea were sold?

d How many drinks of milk were sold?

e Work out the total number of drinks sold.

**◉ Points to remember**

⊙ A **pictogram** uses symbols to represent data.

⊙ A **key** shows how many items of data each symbol stands for.

⊙ A symbol can stand for more than one item of data.

⊙ The symbols are the same size and line up neatly.

## 5 Drawing pictograms

This lesson will help you to represent data in a pictogram.

### Exercise 5

### Example

Ryan asked some of his friends which sport they liked best.

The table shows the results.

| Sport | Number of friends |
|-------|-------------------|
| tennis | 16 |
| swimming | 6 |
| hockey | 11 |
| netball | 8 |

Draw a pictogram to show this information.

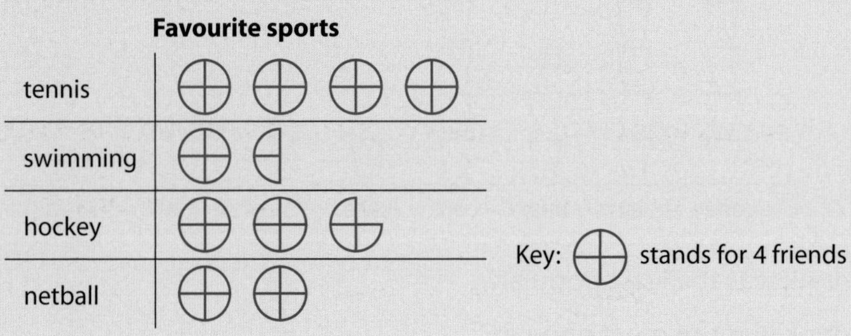

**Favourite sports**

| | |
|---|---|
| tennis | ⊕ ⊕ ⊕ ⊕ |
| swimming | ⊕ ◒ |
| hockey | ⊕ ⊕ ◔ |
| netball | ⊕ ⊕ |

Key: ⊕ stands for 4 friends

①   The table shows how 50 pupils travel to school.

Draw a pictogram to show this data.

Use ⊞ to stand for 4 pupils.

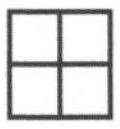

| Form of travel | Number of pupils |
|----------------|------------------|
| walk | 12 |
| bus | 9 |
| train | 6 |
| cycle | 16 |
| car | 7 |

**2** A corner shop sells soft drinks.

**a** The table shows the number of cartons of orange juice sold each day from Monday to Friday of one week.

| Day | Mon | Tues | Wed | Thurs | Fri |
|---|---|---|---|---|---|
| Cartons | 12 | 7 | 8 | 15 | 11 |

Draw a pictogram to represent this information. Use 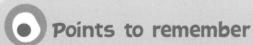 to stand for 2 cartons.

**b** This table shows how many pints of milk sold from Monday to Saturday.

| Day | Mon | Tues | Wed | Thurs | Fri | Sat |
|---|---|---|---|---|---|---|
| Pints | 16 | 16 | 18 | 14 | 17 | 20 |

Draw a pictogram to show this data. Choose a symbol to stand for 4 pints.

**c** This table shows how many fizzy drinks sold from Monday to Saturday.

| Day | Mon | Tues | Wed | Thurs | Fri | Sat |
|---|---|---|---|---|---|---|
| Drinks | 15 | 14 | 18 | 11 | 9 | 6 |

Draw a pictogram to show this data. Choose a symbol to stand for 3 fizzy drinks.

> ## ◉ Points to remember
>
> ⊙ You can use a **pictogram** to represent data.
> ⊙ A pictogram must have a key to show how many items each symbol stands for.
> ⊙ When you draw a pictogram you may need to use part of a symbol.
> ⊙ The symbols should line up neatly.

# 6 Venn and Carroll diagrams

This lesson will help you to use Venn and Carroll diagrams to sort data.

## Exercise 6

Venn and Carroll diagrams are used to sort data into groups according to its properties.

A **Venn diagram** has labelled circles.

A **Carroll diagram** is a rectangular table with labels for the rows and columns.

### Example

This **Venn diagram** shows where some creatures live.

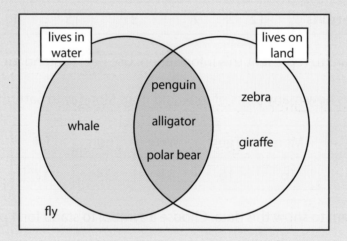

Here is a **Carroll diagram** for the same data.

|  | in water | not in water |
|---|---|---|
| **on land** | penguin<br>alligator<br>polar bear | zebra<br>giraffe |
| **not on land** | whale | fly |

Which creatures live both on land and in water? Penguin, alligator and polar bear.

Which creatures do not live on land or in water? Fly

This table is about some Key Stage 3 pupils and what they like.

| Name | Boy or girl | Age | Favourite food | Favourite sport | Instrument played |
|------|-------------|-----|----------------|-----------------|-------------------|
| Freya | G | 14 | chips | football | flute |
| Arvind | B | 13 | curry | cricket | guitar |
| Oliver | B | 14 | pizza | rugby | saxophone |
| Emil | B | 12 | pizza | football | violin |
| Gemma | G | 14 | curry | tennis | flute |
| Nicole | G | 13 | spaghetti | swimming | violin |
| George | B | 14 | lasagne | football | guitar |
| Will | B | 11 | pizza | football | trombone |
| Paige | G | 14 | curry | swimming | double bass |
| Daisy | G | 13 | curry | football | tuba |

1 Copy and complete this Carroll diagram for the data in the table.

|  | aged 13 | not aged 13 |
|------|---------|-------------|
| **boy** |  |  |
| **not boy** |  |  |

a How many girls aged 13 are there in the group?

b How many boys are there altogether?

2 Copy and complete this Venn diagram about the pupils' favourite foods.

How many pupils did not choose curry or pizza?

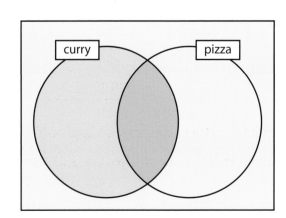

**3** Draw a Venn diagram with two circles.
Label one circle 'football' and the other 'boy'.

Write the pupils' names in the correct places on your diagram.

**4** Draw a Carroll diagram with two rows and two columns.
Label the columns 'string instrument' and 'not string instrument'.
Label the rows 'aged 14' and 'not aged 14'.

Write the pupils' names in the correct places on your diagram.

## Extension problems

**5** Draw your own Venn diagram using the information from the table.
Choose a label for each of the circles using the information in the table.

**6** Draw your own Carroll diagram using the information from the table.

Choose a label for the first column.
Remember that the second column is 'not' the first.

Choose a label for the first row.
The second row is 'not' the first.

## ⊙ Points to remember

- ⊙ **Venn and Carroll diagrams** are for sorting data.
- ⊙ All the data fits in each diagram.
- ⊙ A two-way Carroll diagram has two rows and two columns.
- ⊙ A two-way Venn diagram has two overlapping circles:
    - data in the overlap has both properties;
    - data outside both circles does not have either of the properties.

# How well are you doing?

**Can you:**

- draw and interpret data in lists and tables, frequency tables, tally charts, bar charts, pictograms and Venn and Carroll diagrams?

**1** *2004 Progress Test level 3*

Anna and Jack did a survey together.
They asked people 'What is your favourite sport?'

Anna drew a bar chart to show the results.

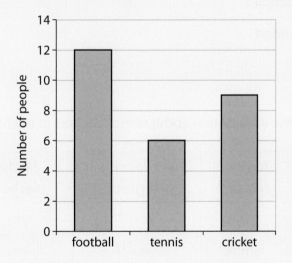

Jack started to draw a pictogram to show the same results.
He drew the result for football.

Copy the pictogram. Complete the results for tennis and cricket.

| football | ◯ ◯ ◯ ◯ |
|----------|---------|
| tennis   |         |
| cricket  |         |

**2** 2003 *Progress Test level 3*

This table shows information about pupils in a class.

|  | Number of boys | Number of girls |
|---|---|---|
| **Right-handed** | 11 | 10 |
| **Left-handed** | 1 | 3 |

a Altogether, how many pupils in the class are left-handed?

b A right-handed girl leaves the class.
A left-handed boy joins the class.

Copy and complete this table for the class now.

|  | Number of boys | Number of girls |
|---|---|---|
| **Right-handed** |  |  |
| **Left-handed** |  |  |

**3** 2004 *Progress Test level 3*

This table shows some information about some teachers in a school.

| Name | Male or female? | Tutor for which year group? | Maths teacher? | Science teacher? |
|---|---|---|---|---|
| Mr Brooks | male | year 7 | yes | no |
| Miss Jones | female | year 9 | no | yes |
| Mrs Patel | female | year 7 | yes | yes |
| Dr Rawley | female | year 8 | yes | no |
| Mr Williams | male | year 11 | no | yes |

Which female teacher teaches maths but not science?

**4** A group of 6 children sorted themselves into these sets.

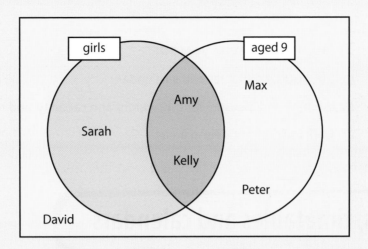

Copy and complete this diagram to show the same information.

|  | girls | not girls |
|---|---|---|
| **aged 9** |  |  |
| **not aged 9** |  |  |

# Measures 3

**This unit will help you to:**

- use clocks, timetables and a calendar;
- estimate and measure length, weight and capacity, and read scales;
- work out perimeters and areas.

## 1 Clocks, timetables and calendars

This lesson will help you to work out how long an event takes.

### Did you know that...?

Thousands of years ago people made marks on animal bones to keep track of time.

The Aztecs made marks on stone.

On 1st October 1949 all countries in the world agreed to use the same date. The whole world now uses the same official calendar.

Some people still celebrate festivals from their old calendar. For example, Chinese people celebrate the start of the **Chinese New Year**.

In 2010, the Chinese New Year begins on 14th February. It is the Year of the Tiger.

### Exercise 1

This rhyme tells you the numbers of days in each month.

> **30 days has September,**
> **April, June and November.**
> **All the rest have 31**
> **Except for February alone.**
> **This has but 28 days clear**
> **And 29 in a leap year.**

Every fourth year is a leap year. A normal year has 365 days. A leap year has 366 days.

## Example 1

Sam and Emma go on holiday for a fortnight to Ireland.
They leave on Tuesday 12th May. When do they come home?

| MAY | | | | | | |
|-----|-----|------|-----|-----|-----|-----|
| Sun | Mon | Tues | Wed | Thu | Fri | Sat |
|  |  |  |  |  | 1 | 2 |
| 3 | 4 | 5 | 6 | 7 | 8 | 9 |
| 10 | 11 | 12 | 13 | 14 | 15 | 16 |
| 17 | 18 | 19 | 20 | 21 | 22 | 23 |
| 24 | 25 | 26 | 27 | 28 | 29 | 30 |
| 31 |  |  |  |  |  |  |

A fortnight is two weeks, which is 14 days.

$12 + 14 = 26$

They return on Tuesday 26th May.

## Example 2

Sam and Emma live 70 minutes away from Newcastle Airport.
They must be at the airport 2 hours early.
The flight leaves at 4:45 pm.

What is the latest time they can leave home?

70 minutes is 1 hour 10 minutes. Adding on 2 hours at the airport gives 3 hours 10 minutes.

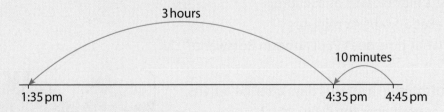

Working backwards from 4:45 pm, this gives a latest leaving time of 1:35 pm.

---

1   a   Which month follows February?

   b   Which is the month before October?

   c   Which month has 28 days?

   d   How many months have 31 days?

   e   Which two months with 31 days are next to each other in the year?

**2**  **a** Paul is flying to Botswana on Wednesday 8th July.
He will arrive home 16 days later.

| JULY | | | | | | |
|---|---|---|---|---|---|---|
| Sun | Mon | Tues | Wed | Thu | Fri | Sat |
|  |  |  | 1 | 2 | 3 | 4 |
| 5 | 6 | 7 | 8 | 9 | 10 | 11 |
| 12 | 13 | 14 | 15 | 16 | 17 | 18 |
| 19 | 20 | 21 | 22 | 23 | 24 | 25 |
| 26 | 27 | 28 | 29 | 30 | 31 |  |

On what day and date will he return from his holiday?

**b** Paul needs to be at the airport by 1:20 pm.
This timetable shows the train times from Hereford to Birmingham Airport.

| Hereford | 10:15 am | 11:15 am | 12:15 pm | 1:15 pm | 2:20 pm |
|---|---|---|---|---|---|
| **Birmingham Airport** | 11:40 am | 12:40 pm | 1:40 pm | 2:40 pm | 3:40 pm |

Which train should he catch from Hereford to arrive in time at Birmingham Airport?

**c** Which is the fastest train on the timetable? How long does it take?

**d** Paul's flight leaves at 3:25 pm.
It takes 5 hours 45 minutes.
At what time does Paul arrive in Botswana?

**e** Paul goes on a safari 4 days after he arrives.
What date does the safari start?

The safari lasts for 3 days.
On what date does it finish?

On the second day of his safari,
Paul sees a elephant.
What day of the week is this?

**f** Paul's flight home takes off at 8:50 am and takes 5 hours and 20 minutes.
At what time does the aeroplane land at Birmingham Airport?

**3** Here is the calendar for October 2008.

| OCTOBER | | | | | | |
|---|---|---|---|---|---|---|
| Sun | Mon | Tues | Wed | Thu | Fri | Sat |
| | | | 1 | 2 | 3 | 4 |
| 5 | 6 | 7 | 8 | 9 | 10 | 11 |
| 12 | 13 | 14 | 15 | 16 | 17 | 18 |
| 19 | 20 | 21 | 22 | 23 | 24 | 25 |
| 26 | 27 | 28 | 29 | 30 | 31 | |

**a** Ram's birthday is on October 16th.
In 2008, his party was on the Sunday after his birthday.
What was the date of his party?

**b** Lisa's birthday is on October 28th.
On what day of the week was her birthday in 2008?

## Extension problem

**4** Here are the start and finish times of some friends doing a sponsored walk.

| | Start time | Finish time |
|---|---|---|
| **Fran** | 2:30 | 3:55 |
| **Daisy** | 2:35 | 4:05 |
| **Andrew** | 2:40 | 4:15 |
| **Simon** | 2:45 | 4:05 |

How much longer did Fran take than Simon?

## Points to remember

- There are 52 weeks in one year.
- A normal year has 365 days.
- Every fourth year is a leap year.
  A leap year has an extra day in February.
- Some months have 31 days and some have 30 days.
  February has 28 or 29 days.

| 60 seconds | = 1 minute |
|---|---|
| 60 minutes | = 1 hour |
| 24 hours | = 1 day |
| 7 days | = 1 week |
| 12 months | = 1 year |

## 2 Reading more scales

This lesson will help you to read different scales.

### Exercise 2

Scales can look very different.

This scale weighs in grams.

This scale weighs in kilograms.

1  **a** How much water is there in the jug?

   **b** Pritam pours 350 ml of water out of the jug.

     How much water is left in the jug?

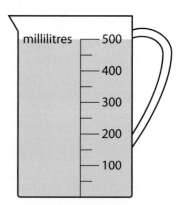

2  **a** How heavy is the parcel?

   **b** Holly adds another parcel to the scales. The second parcel weighs 125 g.

     What is the total weight of both parcels?

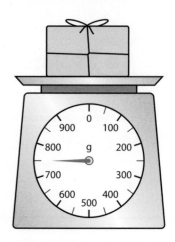

**3** Write the measurement shown by each arrow.

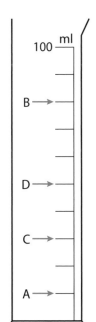
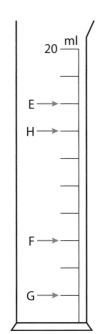
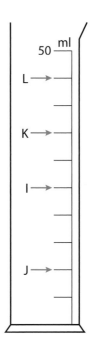
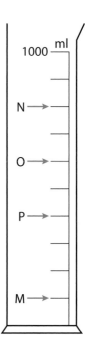

**4** Write the weight shown on each scale.

a

b
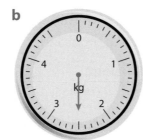

c

d
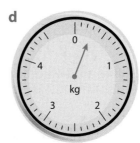

## Extension problem

**5** Estimate the weight shown by each arrow on this scale.

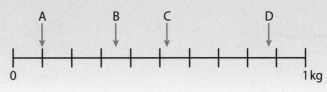

## Points to remember

- Look carefully at a scale to work out the step size.
- Work out the values of the marks close to the pointer.
- If the pointer is between two marks, estimate the reading.
- You can use decimals to record measurements.
- On this scale, there are 10 steps between 2 and 3.
  Each step represents one tenth.
  The pointer shows 2.3.

## 3 Standard metric units 1

This lesson will help you to use kilograms and grams.

### Exercise 3

A kilogram is one thousand grams – **kilo** means one thousand.

Here are two different scales showing the same weight.

A weight of 4600 g                    A weight of 4.6 kg

You can write 4600 g as 4 kg 600 g or 4.6 kg.

1 Estimate the weight of these in kilograms.

    **a** 10 text books                 **b** 10 exercise books

Now weigh the books on the scales. Write their weight in kilograms.

**2** Write the measurement shown on each scale.

a

b

c

d

e

f

**3** You will need a copy of **G1.6 Resource sheet 3.1**.
Draw arrows on the resource sheet to show these measurements.

| a | 900 g | b | 400 g | c | 200 g | d | 825 g |
|---|---|---|---|---|---|---|---|
| e | 50 g | f | 375 g | g | 675 g | h | 350 g |

**4** Copy and complete this table. The first row is done for you.

| | | |
|---|---|---|
| 3400 g | 3 kg 400 g | 3.4 kg |
| 1200 g | … kg … g | … kg |
| … g | 7 kg 300 g | …kg |
| 9100 g | … kg … g | …kg |
| … g | … kg … g | 5.8 kg |
| 700 g | … kg … g | … kg |
| … g | 0 kg 100 g | … kg |

**5** A laptop weighs 1300 g.

   **a** Write this in kilograms and grams.

   **b** Write this in kilograms.

**6** A DVD player weighs 3.5 kg.

   **a** Write this in kilograms and grams.

   **b** Write this in grams.

## Points to remember

⊙ A kilogram is one thousand grams – **kilo** means one thousand.

⊙ The weight 4900 g can be written as 4 kg 900 g.

⊙ The weight 4900 g can also be written 4.9 kg.

⊙ 4900 g = 4 kg 900 g = 4.9 kg

## 4  Standard metric units 2

This lesson will help you to use different metric units to record lengths and capacity as well as writing them in different ways.

### Exercise 4

**Units for measuring length or distance**

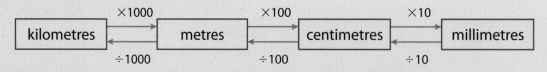

**Units for weighing**

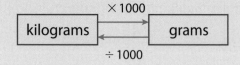

**Units for measuring capacity**

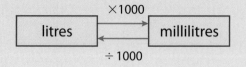

**Examples**

1700 millilitres = 1 litre 700 millilitres = 1.7 litres

620 cm = 6 metres 20 centimetres = 6.2 metres

1. Write which units you would use to measure these objects. Choose from:

millimetres (mm)    centimetres (cm)    metres (m)    kilometres (km)

millilitres (ml)    litres (l)    grams (g)    kilograms (kg)

a   The distance from New York to London
b   The weight of an exercise book
c   The amount of water on a teaspoon
d   The amount of shampoo in a bottle
e   Your height
f   Your weight
g   The width of an exercise book
h   The amount of water in a kettle
i   The amount of petrol in a car
j   The weight of an elephant
k   The distance from the Earth to the Sun
l   The length of a ruler

2. Copy and complete this table. The first row has been done for you.

| | | |
|---|---|---|
| 2300 ml | 2 l 300 ml | 2.3 l |
| 2900 ml | … l … ml | … l |
| … ml | 4 l 100 ml | … l |
| … ml | … l … ml | 7.2 l |
| … ml | 6 l 900 ml | … l |
| 800 ml | … l … ml | … l |

3. Copy and complete this table. The first row has been done for you.

| | | |
|---|---|---|
| 590 cm | 5 m 90 cm | 5.9 m |
| … cm | 7 m 10 cm | … m |
| 230 cm | … m … cm | … m |
| … cm | … m … cm | 4.2 m |
| … cm | … m … cm | 0.9 m |
| 50 cm | … m … cm | … m |
| … cm | 0 m 40 cm | … m |

**4** A car is 4.9 m long.
Copy and complete this sentence.

4.9 m is the same as ......m ......cm.

**5** Another car is 370 cm long.
Copy and complete the sentence.

370 cm is the same as ......m ......cm.

**6** Choose from these measurements.

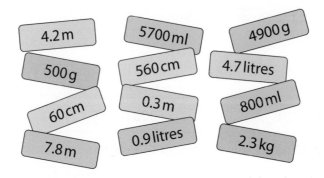

4.2 m

5700 ml

4900 g

500 g

560 cm

4.7 litres

60 cm

0.3 m

800 ml

7.8 m

0.9 litres

2.3 kg

Write a measurement that is the same as:

**a** 5.6 m          **b** 2 kg 300 g          **c** 4700 ml          **d** 5.7 l

**e** 4.9 kg          **f** 30 cm          **g** 2300 g          **h** 5 l 700 ml

**i** 0.6 m          **j** 4 m 20 cm          **k** 0.5 kg          **l** 4 kg 900 g

**m** 900 ml          **n** 780 cm

**7** The world record for running 1500 m is held
by El Guerrouj Hicham of Morocco.

In 1998 he ran 1500 m in 3 minutes 26 seconds.

Write 1500 m in kilometres.

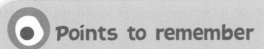
# 5 Perimeter

This lesson will help you to work out the perimeter of shapes.

## Exercise 5

The **perimeter** is the total distance around the edge of a shape.

To find the perimeter, add together the lengths of all the sides.

(1) These rectangles are drawn on a centimetre grid. Work out the perimeter of each rectangle.

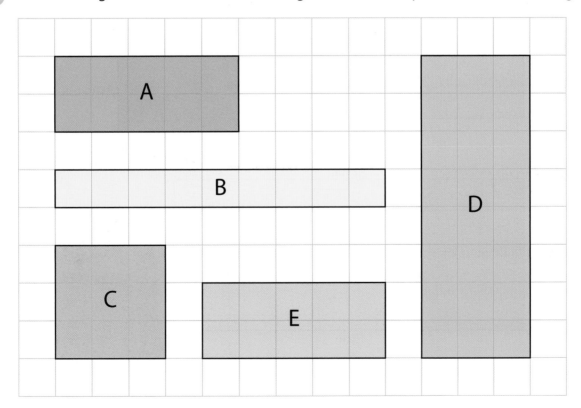

**2** These shapes are drawn on a centimetre grid. Work out the perimeter of each shape.

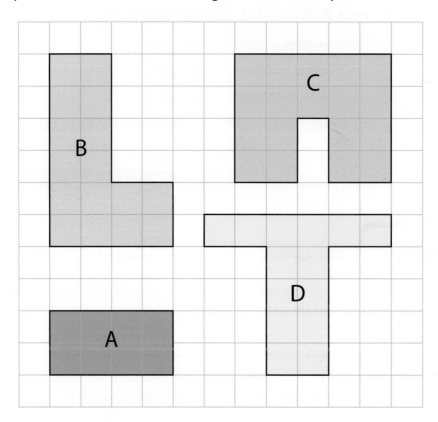

**3** These rectangles are not drawn accurately.
Work out the perimeter of each rectangle.

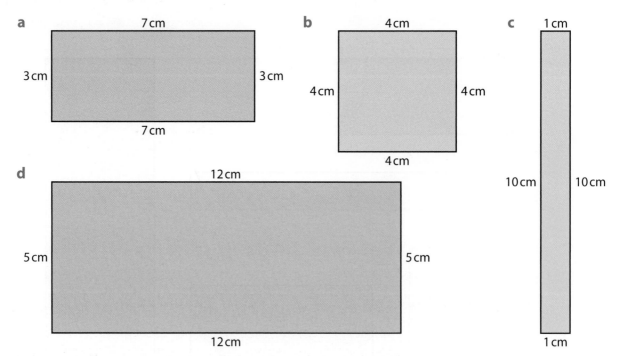

**a**
7 cm
3 cm     3 cm
7 cm

**b**
4 cm
4 cm     4 cm
4 cm

**c**
1 cm
10 cm    10 cm
1 cm

**d**
12 cm
5 cm     5 cm
12 cm

④ For each rectangle, measure the sides.
Use your measurements to calculate the perimeter.

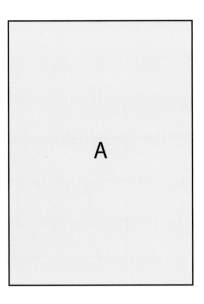

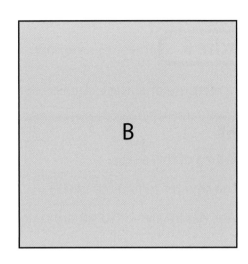

⑤ Use centimetre square paper.
Draw a rectangle with a perimeter of 16 cm.

## Extension problem

⑥ These shapes are not drawn accurately.
Work out the perimeter of each shape.

**a**

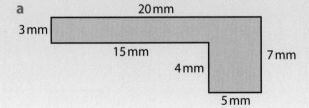

**b**

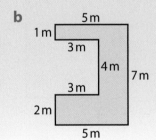

This lesson will help you to work out the areas of shapes by counting squares.

## Exercise 6

Area is a measure of surface. Area is usually measured in square units.

### Example

Find the area of this shape.

Count the squares to find the area.

This shape has an area of 10 square centimetres.

|   | 1 | 2 | 3 | 4 |   |
|---|---|---|---|---|---|
|   |   | 5 | 6 |   |   |
|   | 7 | 8 | 9 | 10 |   |

1 These shapes are drawn on a centimetre grid. Work out the area of each shape.

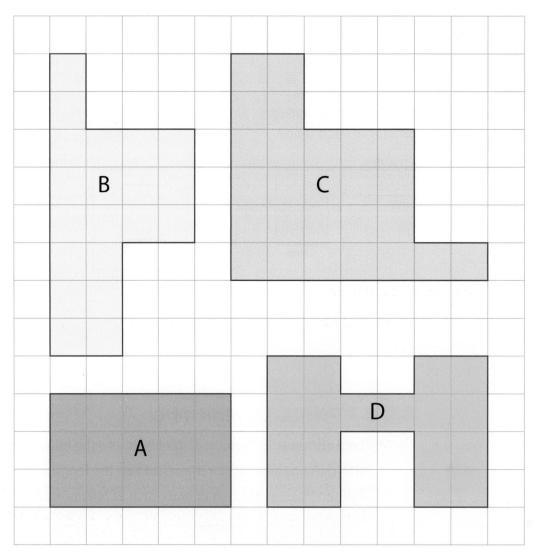

(2) You will need a sheet of centimetre squared paper.

   **a**  Draw a rectangle with an area of 10 square centimetres.

   **b**  Draw a rectangle with an area of 16 square centimetres.

   **c**  Draw a rectangle with an area of 1 square centimetre.

   **d**  Draw a rectangle with an area of 14 square centimetres.

   **e**  Draw a square with an area of 25 square centimetres.

   **f**  Draw a square with an area of 36 square centimetres.

   **g**  Draw a rectangle with an area of 21 square centimetres.

(3) Use another sheet of centimetre squared paper.

   **a**  Draw as many different rectangles as you can with an area of 24 square centimetres.

   **b**  Draw a shape with an area of 20 square centimetres that is not a rectangle or square.

## Extension problems

(4) This shape is drawn on a centimetre grid. Estimate its area.

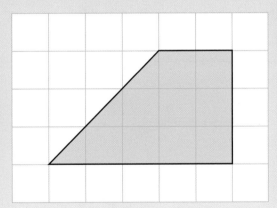

(5) Use centimetre squared paper.

   **a**  Draw four different rectangles each with a perimeter of 16 cm.

   **b**  Write the area of each of your rectangles.

## ⦿ Points to remember

- **Area** is a measure of the surface of a shape.
- To find an area, count the number of squares that the shape covers.
- Area is measured in square units such as square centimetres.

# How well are you doing?

1  a  How much water is in the container?

   b  How many more cups do you need to fill
      the container to the 10 cups mark?

2  For each scale, write the numbers shown by A and B.

   a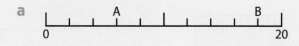

   b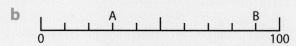

   c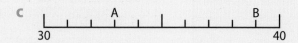

   d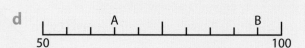

3  Write these lengths in order, starting with the shortest

   0.5 m     130 cm     1.4 m     20 cm

4  *2004 KS1 level 3*

   Harry does English and maths homework each week.
   It takes him a total of two and a half hours.

   He spends 80 minutes doing English homework.
   How many minutes does he spend doing maths homework?

⑤ *2003 KS2 level 3*

Two of these clocks show the same time. Which two clocks are they?

A    B    C    D    E

⑥ *2000 level 3*

Here is a calendar for the last 4 months of the year 2000.

| September | | | | | |
|---|---|---|---|---|---|
| M | | 4 | 11 | 18 | 25 |
| T | | 5 | 12 | 19 | 26 |
| W | | 6 | 13 | 20 | 27 |
| T | | 7 | 14 | 21 | 28 |
| F | 1 | 8 | 15 | 22 | 29 |
| S | 2 | 9 | 16 | 23 | 30 |
| S | 3 | 10 | 17 | 24 | |

| October | | | | | |
|---|---|---|---|---|---|
| M | | 2 | 9 | 16 | 23 | 30 |
| T | | 3 | 10 | 17 | 24 | 31 |
| W | | 4 | 11 | 18 | 25 | |
| T | | 5 | 12 | 19 | 26 | |
| F | | 6 | 13 | 20 | 27 | |
| S | | 7 | 14 | 21 | 28 | |
| S | 1 | 8 | 15 | 22 | 29 | |

| November | | | | | |
|---|---|---|---|---|---|
| M | | 6 | 13 | 20 | 27 |
| T | | 7 | 14 | 21 | 28 |
| W | 1 | 8 | 15 | 22 | 29 |
| T | 2 | 9 | 16 | 23 | 30 |
| F | 3 | 10 | 17 | 24 | |
| S | 4 | 11 | 18 | 25 | |
| S | 5 | 12 | 19 | 26 | |

| December | | | | | |
|---|---|---|---|---|---|
| M | | 4 | 11 | 18 | 25 |
| T | | 5 | 12 | 19 | 26 |
| W | | 6 | 13 | 20 | 27 |
| T | | 7 | 14 | 21 | 28 |
| F | 1 | 8 | 15 | 22 | 29 |
| S | 2 | 9 | 16 | 23 | 30 |
| S | 3 | 10 | 17 | 24 | 31 |

a   What day of the week is December 26th, 2000?

b   A festival starts on the 5th Saturday in September.
    What date in September is that?

c   How many days are there altogether in the last 4 months
    of the year 2000?

# Solving number problems

**This unit will help you to:**

- ◙ solve number problems;
- ◙ record information in a list or table;
- ◙ look for patterns;
- ◙ work systematically.

## 1 Odd and even numbers

This lesson will help you to find properties of odd and even numbers.

### Exercise 1

The **even numbers** are 0, 2, 4, 6, 8, 10, 12, 14, …

The **odd numbers** are 1, 3, 5, 7, 9, 11, 13, 15, …

Even numbers end in **0, 2, 4, 6 or 8**.

Odd numbers end in **1, 3, 5, 7 or 9**.

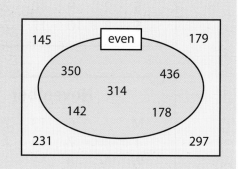

① Which are even?

437    928    1050    1133    825    194

② Which are odd?

2431    853    920    652    1078    525

③ You will need two dice.

Roll the dice.
Investigate different ways of scoring an even total.

Record each way that you find.

(4) Give four examples to show that the sum of two odd numbers is even.

(5) Give four examples to show that the difference of two odd numbers is even.

(6) Give four examples to show that the sum of one odd and one even number is odd.

(7) Play **Odds and evens** with a partner.
You will need a calculator and two packs of cards from 1 to 9.

Spread the cards face down and shuffle them.

### Rules

- One of you is 'Even'. The other is 'Odd'.

- Take turns to go first.

- The first player chooses two cards and makes a two-digit number.
  For example, if you choose 9 and 6, you can make 96 or 69.

- The second player chooses two cards and makes another two-digit number.

- Use the calculator to add the two two-digit numbers.

- If the answer is odd, then 'Odd' scores 1 point.
  If the answer is even, then 'Even' scores 1 point.

- Put the cards back face down, and shuffle.

- It is now the second player's turn to go first.

- The winner is the first to score 6 points.

With 9 and 6, you can make 69 or 96.

(8) Give four examples to show that the difference of between two multiples of 10 is a multiple of 10.

(9) Give four examples to show that double a multiple of 5 is a multiple of 10.

## Extension problems

(10) Give four examples to show that the sum of three odd numbers is odd.

(11) The numbers of three houses are consecutive odd numbers.
The numbers add up to 33.

What are the numbers on the houses?

## 2 Addition problems

This lesson will help you to solve problems by making a table and working systematically.

### Did you know that...?

We have used the signs + for addition and − for subtraction since 1557.

**Robert Recorde** wrote in his book *The Whetstone of Witte* that + means *more* and − means *less*.

Before that, + and − were painted on barrels to show whether or not they were full.

### Exercise 2

1. Harry has three hens. In one week:

    the first and second hens lay 10 eggs altogether;
    the second and third hens lay 14 eggs altogether;
    the first and third hens lay 12 eggs altogether.

    How many eggs does each hen lay?

2. Jyoti, Jessica and Jack each buy a present.

    Jyoti and Jessica spend a total of £7.
    Jessica and Jack spend a total of £14.
    Jyoti and Jack spend a total of £11.

    How much do Jyoti, Jessica and Jack spend altogether?

**(3)** At Rick's café, everything costs a multiple of 10p.

> A cup of tea and a sandwich costs 90p.
> A cup of tea and a scone costs 70p.
> A scone and a sandwich costs £1.

**a** What is the cost of a cup of tea?

**b** What do 2 sandwiches cost?

**c** What do 3 scones cost?

## Points to remember

⊙ Make a table to record information.

⊙ List possibilities systematically.

⊙ Check that the solution satisfies each statement in the problem.

## 3 Using clues

This lesson will help you to use clues about the properties of a number to work out what it is.

## Exercise 3

A **multiple** of a number divides exactly by the number.

60 is a multiple of 3 since 60 ÷ 3 = 20 with no remainder.

### Example 1

Is 78 a multiple of 3?

The answer is a whole number so 78 is a multiple of 3.

### Example 2

Is 78 a multiple of 4?

The answer is not a whole number so 78 is not a multiple of 4.

**Multiples of 3**

| 1 | 2 | 3 | 4 | 5 | 6 | 7 | 8 | 9 | 10 |
|---|---|---|---|---|---|---|---|---|----|
| 11 | 12 | 13 | 14 | 15 | 16 | 17 | 18 | 19 | 20 |
| 21 | 22 | 23 | 24 | 25 | 26 | 27 | 28 | 29 | 30 |
| 31 | 32 | 33 | 34 | 35 | 36 | 37 | 38 | 39 | 40 |
| 41 | 42 | 43 | 44 | 45 | 46 | 47 | 48 | 49 | 50 |
| 51 | 52 | 53 | 54 | 55 | 56 | 57 | 58 | 59 | 60 |
| 61 | 62 | 63 | 64 | 65 | 66 | 67 | 68 | 69 | 70 |
| 71 | 72 | 73 | 74 | 75 | 76 | 77 | 78 | 79 | 80 |
| 81 | 82 | 83 | 84 | 85 | 86 | 87 | 88 | 89 | 90 |
| 91 | 92 | 93 | 94 | 95 | 96 | 97 | 98 | 99 | 100 |

1. Meg's number is a two-digit odd number.
   It is more than 30.
   One digit is double the other.
   What is Meg's number?

2. Ali's number is a two-digit multiple of 5.
   It is greater than 50.
   The difference between the digits is 2.
   What is Ali's number?

3. Olivia's number lies between 50 and 100.
   The number is even.
   One digit is half of the other.
   What is Olivia's number?

4. William's number has two digits.
   The sum of the digits is 9.
   The difference between the digits is 1.
   What is William's number?

5. Said's number is a two-digit even number.
   It lies between 50 and 80.
   The difference in the digits is 4.
   What is Said's number?

6. Razia's number is a two-digit multiple of 4.
   The sum of the digits is 6.
   What is Razia's number?

7. David's number is a two-digit multiple of 10.
   It is a multiple of 3 and a multiple of 4.
   What is David's number?

### Extension problem

8. Charlotte's number is a multiple of 3 and a multiple of 4.
   The sum of its two digits is 9.
   What is Charlotte's number? Find both possibilities.

## Points to remember

⊙ Think about the order in which to use the clues in a problem.

⊙ List possibilities systematically.

⊙ Check that the solution satisfies each statement in the problem.

# 4 Working systematically 1

This lesson will help you to use patterns and to work systematically to solve problems.

## Exercise 4

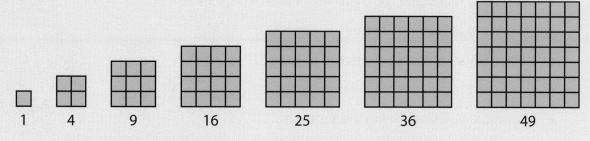

1 | 4 | 9 | 16 | 25 | 36 | 49

This sequence is called the sequence of **square numbers**. Can you see why?

**1** Here is a sequence of shapes made with red and white tiles.
The sequence continues in the same way.

Shape number 1     Shape number 2     Shape number 3     Shape number 4

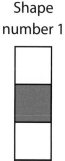  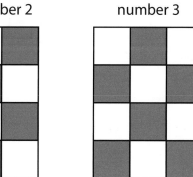 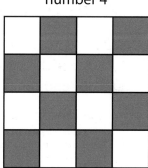

**a** Copy and complete this table.

| Shape number | 1 | 2 | 3 | 4 | 5 | 6 |
|---|---|---|---|---|---|---|
| **Number of red tiles** | | | | | | |
| **Number of white tiles** | | | | | | |
| **Total number of tiles** | | | | | | |

**b** Altogether, how many tiles will be in shape number **10**?

**c** Copy and complete:

The total number of tiles = ...... × the shape number

**②** Here is a sequence of patterns.

Pattern 1     Pattern 2     Pattern 3     Pattern 4

a How many rectangles are there altogether in pattern 1?

b How many rectangles are there in pattern 2?

c How many rectangles are there in pattern 3?

d How many rectangles are there in pattern 4?

e The sequence continues in the same way.
   How many rectangles do you think there will be in pattern 5? Explain why.

**③** Holly makes a sequence of patterns with blue and grey tiles.
Her sequence continues in the same way.

Pattern 1     Pattern 2     Pattern 3     Pattern 4

a Copy and complete this table.

| Pattern number | 1 | 2 | 3 | 4 | 5 | 6 |
|---|---|---|---|---|---|---|
| Number of blue tiles | | | | | | |
| Number of grey tiles | | | | | | |
| Total number of tiles | | | | | | |

b Holly makes a pattern in the sequence using 15 blue tiles.
   How many grey tiles does she use?

c Holly makes another pattern in the sequence using 20 grey tiles.
   How many blue tiles does she use?

d Copy and complete:

The number of grey tiles = ...... × the pattern number

# 5 Working systematically 2

## Did you know that...?

**Al-Khwarizmi** was the keeper of the treasures of the Caliph of Baghdad.

He lived around 800 AD.

Al-Khwarizmi introduced the Hindu numerals 0, 1, 2, 3, 4, 5, 6, 7, 8 and 9 to Europe.

He also used the Arabic word *zephirum*, which became *zero* in today's English.

This lesson will help you to count possibilities systematically.

## Exercise 5

1 Use your digit cards **1, 2, 3, 4, 5** and **6**.
Arrange them in a triangle.

   **a** Make each side of the triangle add up to **9**.

   **b** Make each side of the triangle add up to **10**.

   **c** Make each side of the triangle add up to **11**.

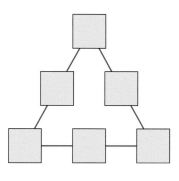

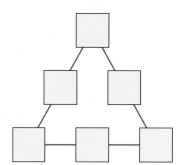

2 Use your digit cards **1, 2, 3, 4, 6** and **7**.
Arrange them in a triangle.

   **a** Make each side of the triangle add up to **11**.

   **b** Make each side of the triangle add up to **12**.

**3** | 1 | 2 | 3 | 4 | 5 | 6 | 7 | 8 |

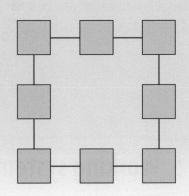

Use your digit cards **1, 2, 3, 4, 5, 6, 7** and **8**.
Arrange them in a square.

**a** Make each side of the square add up to **12**.

**b** Make each side of the square add up to **13**.

---

## Points to remember

⊙ Count possibilities systematically.

⊙ It may help to make a list or table.

⊙ Check that the solution works.

# How well are you doing?

**Can you:**

- ◉ solve number problems?
- ◉ record information in a list or table?
- ◉ identify and use patterns?
- ◉ work systematically?

## Solving number problems (no calculator)

**1**  *2004 level 3*

   **a**  Anna says:

> Multiply any number by three.
>
> The answer must be an odd number.

Give an example to show that Anna is wrong.

   **b**  Jay says:

> Divide any even number by two.
>
> The answer must be an odd number.

Give an example to show that Jay is wrong.

**2**  *2006 Progress Test level 3*

Here is a grid with some numbers shaded.
The grid continues.

Will the number 35 be shaded?

Write **Yes** or **No**.
Explain your answer.

| 1 | 2 | 3 | 4 |
|---|---|---|---|
| 5 | 6 | 7 | 8 |
| 9 | 10 | 11 | 12 |

**3**  *2007 KS2 level 3*

Which of the amounts in this list can be made with exactly three coins?

71p     72p     73p     74p     75p

**4** *2003 level 3*

Here are three different number cards.

**a** Write the biggest number you can show with the cards.

**b** Write the biggest even number you can show with the cards.

**5** *2006 level 3*

Five people played each other at tennis.
The table shows who won each game. For example, when Bob played Ann, Bob won.

| | Ann | | | | |
|---|---|---|---|---|---|
| **Ann** | ✗ | Bob | | | |
| **Bob** | Bob | ✗ | Carl | | |
| **Carl** | Ann | Carl | ✗ | Dan | |
| **Dan** | Ann | Dan | Carl | ✗ | Ed |
| **Ed** | Ann | Bob | Carl | Dan | ✗ |

**a** Ann played four games.
How many games did she win?

**b** Write the name of the person who lost all their games.

**c** Explain why there is a cross (✗) in some of the boxes.

**6** *2003 KS2 level 3*

Katie has these digit cards.
She makes different two-digit numbers with them.

**7**

**5**     **2**

Write all the two-digit numbers Katie can make with them.

# Revision unit 1

**This unit will help you to:**

⊙ revise your work during the year so far;

⊙ answer questions like those in tests and exams;.

⊙ help you to know if you are achieving National Curriculum level 3.

## 1 Place value

This lesson will remind you how to partition, order and round whole numbers.

### Exercise 1

Each digit has a different **value** according to its place.

$4328 = 4000 + 300 + 20 + 8$

**four thousand, three hundred and twenty-eight**

| Thousands | Hundreds | Tens | Units |
|-----------|----------|------|-------|
| 4 | 3 | 2 | 8 |

### Example 1

Put these numbers in order: 268, 52, 305. Start with the smallest.

The smallest number is **52** because it has only **5 tens** and 2 ones.
268 has **2 hundreds** so this is the next smallest number.
305 has **3 hundreds** so this is the biggest number.

The order is 52, 268, 305.

### Example 2

a There are 22 sweets in a bag. What is 22 rounded to the nearest 10?

22 lies between 20 and 30. It is nearer to 20 than to 30.
So 22 is rounded down to 20.

b There are 783 students in a school. What is 783 rounded to the nearest 100?

783 lies between 700 and 800. It is nearer to 800 than 700.
So 783 is rounded up to 800.

**1**  *1998 KS2 level 3*

Look at these digits.

5    0    8    2

**a**  Make the largest number possible with the digits.

**b**  Write your number in words.

**2**  *1998 KS2 level 3*

Here are three digits

**a**  Use all the digits 6, 1 and 3 to write a number that is between 100 and 140.

**b**  Use all the digits 6, 1 and 3 to complete this subtraction.

$$\boxed{\phantom{0}\,|\,\phantom{0}} - \boxed{\phantom{0}} = 25$$

**3**  *2003 level 3*

Here are three number cards.

5    8    3

**a**  What is the biggest number you can make with these cards?

**b**  What is the biggest even number you can make with these cards?

**4**  *2002 KS2 level 3*

Choose three of these number cards. Make an even number greater than 400.

3    8    9    1

**(5)** *2005 level 3*

Write in figures a number that is bigger than one thousand but smaller than one thousand one hundred.

**(6)** *2001 KS2 level 3*

Which three of these multiples of 10 add to make 190?

10    30    50    70    90

**(7)** *2006 KS2 level 3*

Write these numbers in order of size, starting with the smallest.

901    1091    910    109    190

**(8)** *2004 Progress Test level 3*

The diagram shows part of a number grid.
Copy the grid. Fill in the missing numbers.

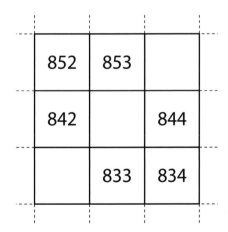

**(9)** *2003 KS2 level 3*

Which of these numbers give 80 when rounded to the nearest 10?
Write all the correct numbers.

84    87    72    76    90

**(10)** *2004 KS2 level 3*

Which of these numbers is closest to 1000?

1060    1049    1100    960    899

11　*2007 Progress Test level 3*

The table shows how many people visit a museum in five weeks.

| Week | Number of visitors | Rounded to the nearest hundred |
|---|---|---|
| 1 | 453 | 500 |
| 2 | 328 | |
| 3 | 557 | |
| 4 | 299 | |
| 5 | 356 | |

Copy and complete the table by rounding each number to the nearest hundred. The first one is done for you.

12　*2005 Progress Test level 3*

A school raised £1758 for charity. A newspaper wrote:

## School raises nearly £1800 for charity

Copy this sentence and fill in the missing number.

> The newspaper rounded £1758 to the nearest …………

13　*2005 Progress Test level 4*

Which of the numbers below is four thousand and seven? Write it in your book.

47　　　　407　　　　4007

40 007　　　400 007

## Points to remember

- You can partition four-digit numbers like this:

  $7824 = 7000 + 800 + 20 + 4$

- To order numbers, look at the values of the digits, starting from the left.
- Round up fives, e.g. 45 rounds to 50.

# 2 Adding and subtracting

This lesson will remind you how to add and subtract numbers.

## Exercise 2

You can **add** or **subtract** by writing numbers in columns.
Line up the units under the units, the tens under the tens, and so on.

### Example 1

Calculate 417 + 259.

Use rounding to estimate the answer. Estimate: 400 + 300 = 700

```
  417
+ 259
      16  add the ones
      60  add the tens
     600  add the hundreds
     676  find the total
```

It may be quicker to do it like this.

```
  417
+ 259
  676
    1
```

### Example 2

Calculate 643 − 347.

Use rounding to estimate the answer. Estimate: 600 − 300 = 30

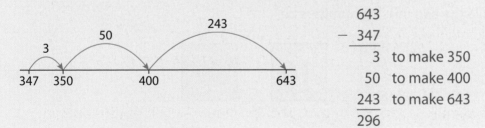

```
  643
− 347
      3  to make 350
     50  to make 400
    243  to make 643
    296
```

Do these questions **without using your calculator**.

**(1)** *2007 level 3*

Work out:

**a** 64 + 57                      **b** 64 − 57

**(2)** *2007 Progress Test level 3*

Work out the answers to these calculations.

**a** 257 + 649                **b** 541 − 382

(3) *2005 level 3*

    **a** Add together 147 and 376        **b** Subtract 36 from 218

(4) *2003 level 3*

    **a** What number should you add to 28 to make 100?

    **b** What number should you subtract from 100 to make 78?

Work out:

    **c** $1048 + 208$        **d** $4828 - 480$

(5) *2005 Progress Test level 3*

Copy and fill in the missing numbers.

    **a** $46 + \square = 73$        **b** $55 - \square = 29$

(6) *2004 Progress Test level 3*

    **a** The numbers on these three cards should have a total of 50. What is the missing number?

    **b** The numbers on these three cards should have a total of 50. What could the two missing numbers be?

(7) *2006 Progress Test level 3*

Copy and fill in the missing numbers.

    **a** $3 + 11 = 4 + \square$        **b** $15 + 8 = 5 + \square$

    **c** $40 - 10 = 50 - \square$        **d** $25 - 8 = 9 + \square$

(8) *2006 Progress Test level 3*

Copy and fill in the missing numbers.

    **a** $972 - \square = 476$        **b** $\square - 128 = 415$

**Extension problems**

 **9** *2003 KS2 level 3*

Here are five digit cards.

**1** **2** **3** **4** **5**

Use all five digit cards once to make this sum correct.

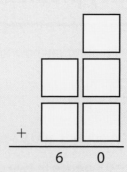

```
      [ ]
 [ ]  [ ]
 [ ]  [ ]
+_____
  6    0
```

 **10** *2002 level 3*

The tables show how much a week's holiday costs.

| May | |
|---|---|
| Week beginning | Cost |
| 4 May | £194 |
| 11 May | £196 |
| 18 May | £196 |
| 25 May | £209 |

| June | |
|---|---|
| Week beginning | Cost |
| 1 June | £304 |
| 8 June | £219 |
| 15 June | £234 |
| 22 June | £259 |
| 29 June | £269 |

| July | |
|---|---|
| Week beginning | Cost |
| 6 July | £279 |
| 13 July | £289 |
| 20 July | £319 |
| 27 July | £334 |

**a** The week beginning **29 June** costs more than the week beginning **22 June**.
How much more?

**b** A woman pays for the weeks beginning **4 May**, **11 May** and **18 May**.
A man pays for the weeks beginning **13 July** and **20 July**.
The man pays more than the woman.
How much more?
Show your working.

 **Points to remember**

- To add or subtract numbers in columns, line up the units under units, the tens under tens, and so on.

- Count up from the smaller to the larger number to subtract, find the difference, or find how many more or how many less.

- To find the sum, add all the numbers.

- To find a difference, take the smaller number from the bigger number.

## 3 Money problems

This lesson will remind you how to do money calculations with and without a calculator.

### Exercise 3

£4.93 means 4 pounds and 93 pence.

You can write **93 pence** in two different ways: in pence as **93p** or in pounds as **£0.93**.

To enter 93p **in pounds** (£), key in: ⓪ ⊙ ⑨ ③

To enter 93p **in pence**, key in: ⑨ ③

If the answer to a calculation is in pounds:

| 8.2 | in the display means £8.20

| 0.47 | in the display means 47p

| 0.04 | in the display means 4p

To add or subtract pounds and pence **without a calculator**, write them in columns.
Line up the points under each other.

### Example

£4.15 − 74p = £4.15 − £0.74

$$\begin{array}{r} £ \\ 4.15 \\ -0.74 \\ \hline 3.41 \end{array}$$

Do questions 1 to 3 **without a calculator**. Show your working.

① *2007 Progress Test level 3*

    **a** Jack buys four apples. He pays with a £2 coin. He gets £1.20 change.
       How much does one apple cost?

    **b** Oranges cost 15p each. Raj has a £1 coin.
       What is the greatest number of oranges Raj can buy with £1?

② *2005 Progress Test level 3*

    Lisa buys three pens.
    She gives the shopkeeper £5 and gets £1.10 change.
    What is the cost of one pen?

**3** *2000 level 3*

## Museum

*entrance fee
£1.20 per person*

a 240 people paid the entrance fee on Monday.

How much money is that altogether?

b The museum took £600 in entrance fees on Friday.

How many people paid to visit the museum on Friday?
Show your working.

For the rest of the questions, you may **use a calculator**.

**4** *2003 level 3*

Alice and Ben each buy a bicycle but they pay in different ways.

Alice pays **£179.99**.

Ben pays **£8.62** every week for **24** weeks.

Ben pays more than Alice. How much more?
Show your working.

**5** *2001 level 3*

a Joe bought a box of cards for £6.80.
He paid with a £10 note.
How much change should Joe get?

b Sanjay bought 15 boxes of cards.
Each box cost £6.80.
How much did Sanjay pay for the boxes altogether?

c Amy paid £26.60 for some packets of cards.
Each packet cost £1.90.
How many packets did Amy buy?

(6) *2004 level 3*

A shop sells sports equipment.

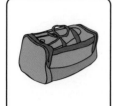
sports bag
**£12.99**

trampette
**£17.99**

basketball stand
**£169**

tennis racket
**£14.99**

football
**£5.99**

a   Mr Adams pays for a sports bag and a basketball stand.
    Altogether, how much does he pay?

b   Mrs Brown has £20. She pays for two footballs. How much change should she get?

c   Mrs Cooke has £50. How many tennis rackets can she buy?

(7) *2005 level 3*

There are 15 rulers in a box.
One box of rulers costs £1.45.

a   How many rulers are there in 8 boxes?

b   How much do 8 boxes cost?

c   How much do 30 rulers cost?

d   How many boxes of rulers could you buy for £7.25?

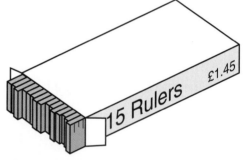

## Extension problem

(8) *2007 level 4*

Leena buys balloons, hats and masks for a party.
Copy and complete the table. Fill in the missing numbers.

|  | Cost of each (£) | Number bought | Total cost (£) |
|---|---|---|---|
| Packets of balloons | 4.95 | 5 | ............ |
| Hats | 3.20 | ............ | 41.60 |
| Masks | ............ | 10 | 19.50 |
|  |  |  | Total:......... |

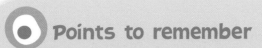

## Points to remember

⊙ Read problems carefully.

⊙ Change amounts all to £ or all to pence.

⊙ Decide what calculation to do and write it down.

⊙ Decide whether to use a mental, written or calculator method.

⊙ When you use a calculator, think about how to enter numbers and interpret the display. Jot down answers to interim steps.

⊙ When you write the final answer, include any units.

## 4 Properties of shapes

This lesson will remind you about right angles and lines of symmetry.

 **Did you know that...?**
You can often see lines of symmetry in the environment.

## Exercise 4

Many mathematical shapes have a **line of symmetry**.

A rectangle · · · · · · · · · An equilateral triangle · · · · · · · A square

 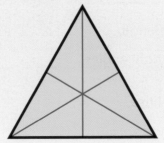 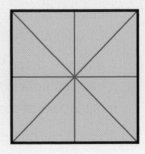

Shapes sometimes have a **right angle**, which is the same as a quarter turn.

**1** *2004 Progress Test level 3*

Look at the shape drawn on the square grid.

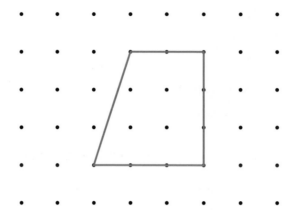

For each of these statements, write **True** or **False**.

a The shape has exactly 2 right angles.

b The shape has 2 pairs of parallel lines.

c The shape has one line of symmetry.

d The shape is a quadrilateral.

**2** *2002 level 3*

Look at the shape on the right.
Copy and complete these sentences.

a The shape has … right angles.

b It has … straight sides.

c It has… pairs of parallel lines.

d … of the sides are the same length.

**3** *2002 level 3*

You need some squared paper. Draw each of these shapes.

a A shape has 4 right angles.
It has 4 straight sides.
All 4 sides are the same length.

b A different shape has 4 right angles.
It has 4 straight sides.
It has 2 pairs of parallel lines.

c A shape has no right angles.
It has 4 straight sides.
It has 2 pairs of parallel lines.

**4** *2004 level 3*

When you fold a square along a diagonal, you see a triangle.

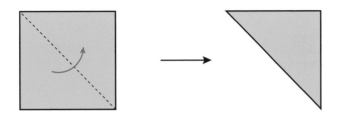

What do you see when you fold a rectangle along a diagonal?

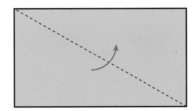

Write down the letter of the correct shape picture below.

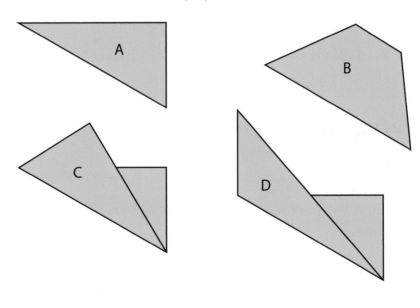

**5** *2003 Progress Test level 3*

Look at this shape.
Copy and complete these sentences.

**a** The shape is a square so the sides must be ...............................................................

**b** The shape is a square so the angles must be ...........................................................

**(6)** *2007 Progress Test level 3*

For each of these statements, write **True** or **False**.

a All rectangles have four sides.

b All rectangles have four equal sides.

c Some rectangles have no right angles.

d All rectangles have at least one line of symmetry.

**(7)** *2005 KS2 level 3*

Here are some shaded shapes on a square grid.

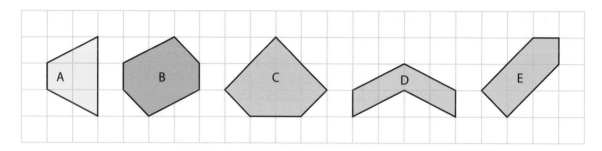

a Write the letters of the two shapes which are hexagons.

b Write the letters of the two shapes which have right angles.

c Write the letter of the shape that has no line of symmetry.

**(8)** *2003 KS2 level 3*

This grid has eight squares shaded in.

Copy the grid on squared paper.

Shade in two more squares to make a symmetrical pattern.

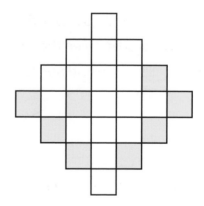

# 5 Tables, graphs and charts

This lesson will remind you how to represent and interpret data in tables, lists and bar charts.

## Exercise 5

**Tables** are useful ways of organising data.

The table on the right shows how some children in a primary school class travelled to school.

The table shows that one came to school by train. Most children walked or came by car.

| Transport | Frequency |
|-----------|-----------|
| walk | 16 |
| cycle | 2 |
| car | 12 |
| bus | 4 |
| train | 0 |

A **bar chart** is a way of showing data to make it easy to interpret.

The bar chart on the right shows the same information as in the table above.

In a bar chart:
- both axes have labels;
- all the bars are the same width;
- there is a gap between the bars;
- the bars can be drawn horizontally or vertically.

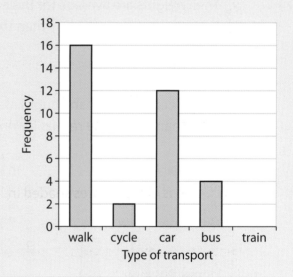

1. *2000 Key Stage 2 level 3*

This table shows the numbers of children who went walking, sailing or climbing.

|          | May | June | July |
|----------|-----|------|------|
| walking  | 25  | 80   | 75   |
| sailing  | 15  | 42   | 50   |
| climbing | 18  | 27   | 23   |

a  How many children went sailing in May, June and July altogether?

b  How many more children went walking in June than climbing in June?

**2** *2005 level 3*

The table shows the average heights of boys and girls of different ages.

| Age (years) | Average height for boys (cm) | Average height for girls (cm) |
|:---:|:---:|:---:|
| 7 | 122 | 121 |
| 9 | 134 | 133 |
| 11 | 143 | 144 |
| 13 | 155 | 155 |
| 15 | 169 | 162 |

**a** What is the average height for girls aged 9 years old?

**b** A boy and a girl are both 15 years old.
Their heights are average for their age.
How much taller is the boy than the girl?

**3** *2003 level 3*

A school records how many pupils are late each day.
The bar charts show the results for one week.

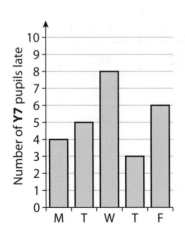 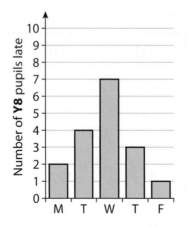 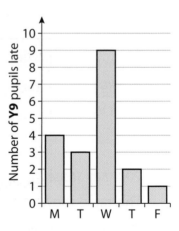

**a** Altogether, how many pupils were late on Monday?

**b** Altogether, how many lates were recorded for Y9 pupils?

**c** The school bus broke down on one of the days.
Which day do you think that was? Explain why you chose that day.

**4** *2005 level 3*

The table shows information about the Paralympic Games.

| Year | Number of countries that took part | Country where the games took place | Number of people that took part |
|------|-----------------------------------|------------------------------------|--------------------------------|
| 1960 | 23 | Italy | 400 |
| 1980 | 42 | Holland | 2500 |

a More countries took part in 1980 than in 1960. How many more?

b More people took part in 1980 than in 1960. How many more?

c In the year 2000, the games took place in Australia.
81 more countries took part in 2000 than in 1980.
How many countries took part in 2000?

d 1324 more people took part in 2000 than in 1980.
How many people took part in 2000?

**5** *1995 level 3*

These are the results of a boys' long jump competition.
The table shows how far they jumped in centimetres.

|       | 1st jump | 2nd jump | 3rd jump | 4th jump |
|-------|----------|----------|----------|----------|
| Akira | 319 | 198 | 352 | 462 |
| Bob   | 268 | 196 | 465 | 264 |
| Carl  | 324 | 411 | 171 | 298 |
| Deri  | 209 | 212 | 304 | 456 |
| Edward| 173 | 177 | 325 | 318 |

For example, Deri jumped 304 cm on his 3rd jump.

a How far did Edward jump on his 2nd jump?

b Who was in the lead after all the 1st jumps?

c Which boys jumped more than 200 cm on the 2nd jump?

d Who improved with every jump?

e Who always jumped further than Edward?

For questions **6** and **7** you will need **R1.1 Resource sheet 5.1**.

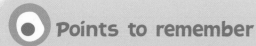

## Points to remember

- Lists and tables allow you to:
  - compare information;
  - look for differences and similarities;
  - look for patterns.
- Bar charts help you to spot patterns and to compare sets of data.
- The scale on a bar chart helps you to interpret the chart.

# Revision unit 2

**This unit will help you to:**

- revise your work during the year so far;
- answer questions like those in tests and exams;
- help you to know if you are achieving National Curriculum level 3.

## 1 Sequences

This lesson will remind you how to extend and complete number sequences.

### Exercise 1

This is a **sequence** of numbers: **5, 10, 15, 20, ….**
The numbers go up in steps of **5**.

The **rule** to find the next term is '**add 5**'.
Here is the same sequence on a number line

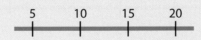

① *2007 level 3*
Each rule below makes a sequence.
Use the rule to write the next two numbers for each sequence.

a **Rule:** Add 3 to the last number

   **Sequence:**    2    5    8    …    …

b **Rule:** Double the last number then add 1

   **Sequence:**    2    5    11    …    …

c **Rule:** Multiply the last number by 3 then subtract 1

   **Sequence:**    2    5    14    …    …

**2** *2003 KS2 level 3*

Copy this sequence and fill in the missing numbers.

64    32    16    ...    4    ...

**3** *1998 KS2 level 3*

Copy and complete this sequence.

480    240    ...    60    ...    15

**4** *1997 level 3*

**a** Look at this part of a number line.

Copy and complete this sentence.

**The numbers go up in steps of** ...

**b** Draw this number line and fill in the three missing numbers.

**c** Draw this number line and fill in the three missing numbers.

**d** Draw this number line and fill in the two missing numbers.

Copy and complete this sentence.

**The numbers go up in steps of** ...

**e** Draw this number line and fill in the three missing numbers.

Copy and complete this sentence.

**The numbers go up in steps of** ...

**5** *2007 Progress Test level 3*

Copy this number sequence. Write the missing numbers in the boxes.

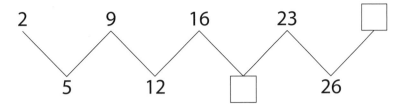

2    9    16    23    ☐

5    12    ☐    26

**6** *1998 KS2 level 3*

This number square is torn.

What was the largest number
on the square before it was torn?

| 6 | 12 | 18 | 24 |
|---|----|----|----|
| 30 | 36 | 42 | |
| 54 | 60 | | |
| 78 | | | |

**Extension problem**

 **7** *2006 level 4*

**a** These rules show how to get from one number to the next in these sequences.
Use the rules to copy and complete each sequence.

  **i** **Rule:** Add 8

  **Sequence:**   4    12    ...    ...

  **ii** **Rule:** Multiply by 3

  **Sequence:**   4    12    ...    ...

**b** A sequence of numbers starts like this:    30   22   18

Could the rule be 'subtract 8'?
Write **Yes** or **No**. Explain your answer.

## ◉ Points to remember

- ⊙ A **sequence** of numbers follows a rule.
- ⊙ If a sequence goes up or down in equal steps, you can work out the rule
  and the next terms.
- ⊙ **Multiples of 3** are numbers that divide exactly by 3.
- ⊙ The rule for the sequence of multiples of 3 is 'add 3'.

# 2 Multiplying and dividing

This lesson will remind you how to multiply and divide numbers.

## Exercise 2

You can **multiply** numbers using a grid.

### Example 1

Calculate 235 × 4.

First, estimate the answer. It will be a bit more than 200 × 4 = 800.

235 = 200 + 30 + 5      Split 235 into **200 + 30 + 5**.

| × | 200 | 30 | 5 |
|---|-----|-----|---|
| 4 | 800 | 120 | 20 |

Make a grid.
Multiply 200 by 4 to get 800
Multiply 30 by 4 to get 120
Multiply 5 by 4 to get 20

800 + 120 + 20 = 940      Add 800, 120 and 20.

**Answer: 235 × 4 = 940**

---

You can **divide** numbers using a 'chunking' method.

### Example 2

Calculate 115 ÷ 5. This means work out how many 5s make 115.

First, estimate the answer. Work out:

5 × **10** = 50
5 × **20** = 100
5 × **30** = 150

**100** and **150** trap the number 115.

This tells you that the answer to 115 ÷ 5 is between **20** and **30**.

```
  5)115
-  100   5 × 20    First take away 20 fives, or 100.
    15             This leaves 15.
    15   5 × 3     Then take away 3 fives, or 15.
     0   5 × 23    There is 0 left.
                   Altogether you have taken away 23 fives.
```

**Answer: 115 ÷ 5 = 23**

Do questions **1** to **5 without a calculator**. Show your working.

**(1)** *2007 level 3*

Look at these numbers.

12      15      16      20      30

   **a**  Write all of the numbers above that **divide by 5** with no remainder.

   **b**  Write all of the numbers above that **divide by 3** with no remainder.

   **c**  Write all of the numbers above that **divide by 15** with no remainder.

**(2)** *2006 level 3*

Work out $37 \times 5$.

**(3)** *2004 level 3*

   **a**  Multiply 49 by 3.           **b**  Divide 160 by 4.

**(4)** *2000 level 3*

   **a**  Multiply 36 by 4.           **b**  Divide 135 by 5.

**(5)** *2003 Progress Test level 3*

Copy and complete these calculations to make them correct.

   **a**  $\square \times 5 = 100$           **b**  $100 \div \square = 25$

**(6)** *2007 level 3*

Here is part of the 36 times table.

Use the 36 times table to help you to work out the missing numbers.

   **a**  $288 \div 8 = \ldots$

   **b**  $180 \div 36 = \ldots$

   **c**  $11 \times 36 = \ldots$

$$1 \times 36 = 36$$
$$2 \times 36 = 72$$
$$3 \times 36 = 108$$
$$4 \times 36 = 144$$
$$5 \times 36 = 180$$
$$6 \times 36 = 216$$
$$7 \times 36 = 252$$
$$8 \times 36 = 288$$
$$9 \times 36 = 324$$
$$10 \times 36 = 360$$

**7** *2007 Progress Test level 3*

Molly wants to decorate some cakes.
Each cake will have 3 cherries.
Molly has 48 cherries.
How many cakes can she decorate?

For questions **8** to **11** you may **use a calculator**.

**8** *2007 KS2 level 3*

   **a** 50 pupils need two pencils each.
      There are 20 pencils in a box.

      How many boxes of pencils are needed?

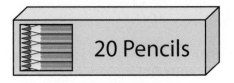

   **b** 50 pupils need one pen each.
      Pens are sold in packs of 4.

      How many packs of pens need to be bought?

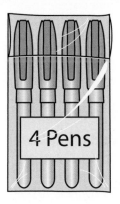

**9** *2006 KS2 level 3*

What is the missing number?
$\square \times 35 = 140$

**10** *1999 level 3*

What is the missing number?

   **a** $26 \times \square = 962$         **b** $\square \div 24 = 16$

**11** *2000 level 3*

   **a** Multiply 69 by 14, then add 34.

   **b** Add 94 to half of 778.

   **c** How much less than 1000 is $59 \times 16$?

## 3 Fractions

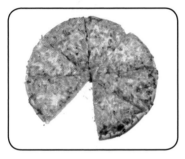

$\frac{7}{8}$ of a pizza

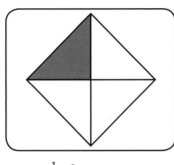

$\frac{1}{4}$ of a square

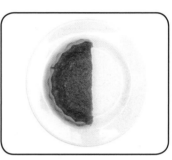

$\frac{1}{2}$ of a treacle tart

This lesson will remind you how to find fractions.

### Exercise 3

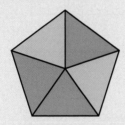

This shape is divided into 5 equal triangles.

**2** out of **5** triangles are blue, so $\frac{2}{5}$ of the shape is blue.

**3** out of **5** triangles are red, so $\frac{3}{5}$ of the shape is red.

To find $\frac{1}{2}$, divide by 2.

To find $\frac{1}{3}$, divide by 3.

To find $\frac{1}{4}$, divide by 4.

**Example:**     Find $\frac{1}{5}$ of £30.

To find $\frac{1}{5}$, divide by 5.

$30 ÷ 5 = 6$, so $\frac{1}{5}$ of £30 is £6.

1   *2003 KS1 level 3*

Copy the shape.
Shade more squares so that $\frac{3}{4}$ of the shape is shaded.

(2) *1998 KS2 level 3*

Which two of these shapes have three quarters shaded?

| A | B | C | D | E |
|---|---|---|---|---|

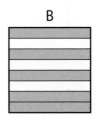 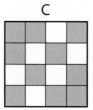 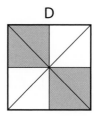 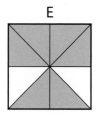

(3) *2007 KS2 level 3*

Which two of these shapes have exactly half shaded?

| A | B | C | D | E |
|---|---|---|---|---|

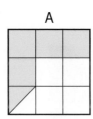 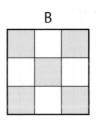 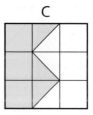 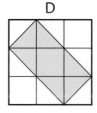 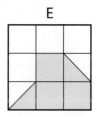

(4) *2005 level 3*

The square grid is divided into **quarters**.

**a** Draw the square grid on squared paper. Draw lines on it to divide it into quarters in a different way.

**b** Draw another copy of the square grid. Draw lines on it to divide it into eighths.

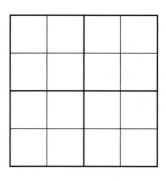

(5) *1997 level 3*

Sue and Ben each have 12 biscuits.

**a** Sue eats a quarter of her biscuits. How many biscuits does Sue eat?

**b** Ben eats 6 of his 12 biscuits. What fraction of his biscuits does Ben eat?

**c** How many biscuits are left altogether?

**6** *2002 KS2 level 3*

Which two of these cards give a total of 5?

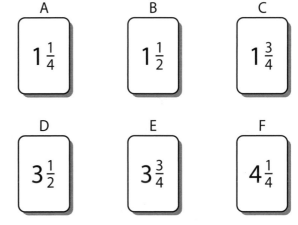

A $1\frac{1}{4}$

B $1\frac{1}{2}$

C $1\frac{3}{4}$

D $3\frac{1}{2}$

E $3\frac{3}{4}$

F $4\frac{1}{4}$

**7** *2003 KS2 level 3*

Which two of these fractions are greater than one half?

$$\frac{1}{8} \quad \frac{6}{10} \quad \frac{5}{8} \quad \frac{3}{10}$$

**8** *1998 KS2 level 3*

$\frac{3}{8}$ of a class are boys. What fraction of the class are girls?

## Extension problems

**9** *2006 Progress Test level 4*

Copy these and fill in the missing numbers.

a $\frac{1}{5}$ of 20 = ☐

b $\frac{3}{4}$ of 20 = ☐

**10** *2006 Progress Test level 4*

Think about the fraction $\frac{1}{5}$

How many of them add to make 1?

 **Points to remember**

- The top number of a fraction is the **numerator**.
  The bottom number is the **denominator**.
- If a shape has 8 equal parts and 3 parts are shaded, then $\frac{3}{8}$ is shaded.
- Find fractions of numbers by dividing, e.g. to find one third, divide by 3.

# 4 Measures

This lesson will remind you how to work out time intervals and estimate and measure using metric units.

  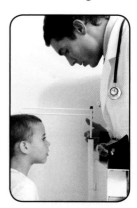

## Exercise 4A

### Example

Complete this table of equivalent measures.

| 1.6 m | 1 m and … cm | … cm |
|---|---|---|
| … m | 5 m and 20 cm | … cm |
| 5.7 kg | … kg and 700 grams | … grams |
| … litres | 2 litres and … ml | 2300 ml |

Here is the completed table.

| 1.6 m | 1 m and **60** cm | **160** cm |
|---|---|---|
| **5.2** m | 5 m and 20 cm | **520** cm |
| 5.7 kg | **5** kg and 700 grams | **5700** grams |
| **2.3** litres | 2 litres and **300** ml | 2300 ml |

① *1999 KS2 level 3*

Choose a word from the box to copy to complete each sentence.

a You can measure how tall you are in …………

b You can measure how heavy you are in …………

c You can measure how much you drink in …………

**kilograms**

**litres**

**centimetres**

② *1997 KS1 level 3*

How long do you think this line is?

Choose from:

5 cm      16 cm      8 cm      12 cm      20 cm

③ *2003 KS2 level 3*

Which two of these sentences could be true?

A  Adam's pencil is 12 centimetres long.

B  Leah is 12 metres tall.

C  Jake's glass holds 12 litres of milk.

D  Kate's younger sister weighs 12 kilograms.

④ *2007 Progress test level 3*

Raj is making a cake.

The scales show how much flour he uses.

How much flour does Raj use?

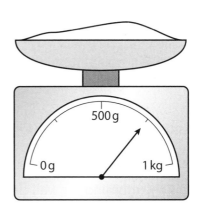

⑤ *1998 KS2 level 3*

Write the number shown by the red arrow.

An **analogue** clock

This clock shows **8 o'clock**.

A **digital** clock

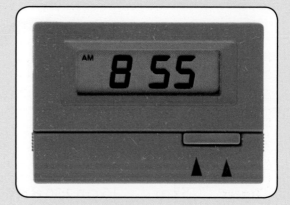

This clock shows **8:55**.

## Example

Emily leaves work at 5:15. She gets home at 7 o'clock. How long does her journey take?

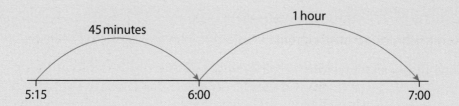

The journey takes 1 hour 45 minutes.

---

**1**  *2003 level 3*

Early in the morning my wall clock shows this time:

My digital clock shows the same time as my wall clock.

Write what time my digital clock is showing.

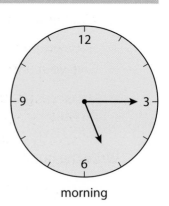

morning

**2**  *2007 KS2 level 3*

The time is 10:35 am.
Kate says:

> 'The time is closer to 11:00 am than to 10:00 am'.

Explain why Kate is correct.

(3) *2007 level 3*

The table shows feeding times for some animals in a zoo.

| | Start of feeding times | | | Length of feeding times |
|---|---|---|---|---|
| **Elephants** | 11:15 am | 2:15 pm | 3:20 pm | 15 minutes |
| **Giraffes** | 12:20 pm | 2:30 pm | | 15 minutes |
| **Otters** | 1:00 pm | | | 10 minutes |
| **Seals** | 1:00 pm | 4:00 pm | | 10 minutes |
| **Tigers** | 2:30 pm | | | 30 minutes |

a The first feeding time for giraffes starts at 12:20 pm. At what time does it finish?

b One feeding time finishes at 3:00 pm. Which animal's feeding time is this?

(4) *1996 level 3*

Derek is going from Croxton to Braytown by bus.
The timetable shows what time buses leave Croxton and arrive at Braytown.

| **Bus Timetable:** Croxton to Braytown | | | | | |
|---|---|---|---|---|---|
| **Croxton:** *depart* | 08:30 | 08:45 | 09:20 | 09:45 | 10:30 |
| **Braytown:** *arrive* | 09:15 | 09:30 | 10:05 | 10:30 | 11:15 |

a Derek catches the 08:45 bus from Croxton.
What time does he arrive in Braytown?

b How long does the bus journey take?
Give your answer as a number of minutes.

c Derek caught the 08:45 bus from Croxton.
He took 15 minutes to get from his house to the bus stop.
He waited 5 minutes for the bus to come.
What time did Derek leave his house?

d Ruth is going from Croxton to Braytown by bus as well.
Ruth must get to Braytown by 10:20.
Which buses could she catch?

e Ruth is 15 minutes too late for the 08:45 from Croxton.
She catches the next bus instead.
How long does Ruth wait for the next bus?

## Extension problem

 **5** *2007 Progress Test level 4*

The table shows the times that street lights come on one night and go off the next morning.

| City | Time the lights come **on** (pm) | Time the lights go **off** (am) |
|------|:---:|:---:|
| Belfast | 6:45 | 6:13 |
| Glasgow | 6:40 | 6:05 |
| London | 6:21 | 5:51 |
| Manchester | 6:30 | 5:59 |
| Newcastle | 6:28 | 5:55 |

**a** Copy and complete the sentence below.

In Manchester, the lights come on 15 minutes earlier than they do in ..................

**b** In Glasgow, the lights go off later than they do in Newcastle. How much later?

**c** In Ashford the lights come on at 6:20 pm. The lights go off $11\frac{1}{2}$ hours later. What time do the lights go off?

---

## ◉ Points to remember

- ⊙ Metric units for length are millimetres (mm), centimetres (cm), metres (m) and kilometres (km).
- ⊙ Metric units for mass are grams (g) and kilograms (kg).
- ⊙ Metric units for capacity are millilitres (ml) and litres (l).
- ⊙ A length like 4.6 m can be written in mixed units as 4 m 60 cm or in centimetres as 460 cm.
- ⊙ The day is divided into am and pm.

# 5 Charts and graphs

This lesson will help you to represent and interpret data in Venn diagrams, Carroll diagrams and pictograms.

## Exercise 5A

A **pictogram** uses symbols or pictures to represent information.
This pictogram shows information about cars in a car park.

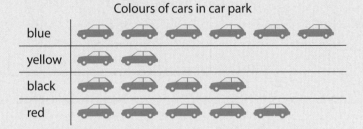

Colours of cars in car park

Key: 🚗 stands for 2 cars

A **key** is used to explain what each symbol represents.

The symbol may represent more than one item of data. To represent only one item of data, part of the symbol is used.

---

**1** *2006 Progress Test level 3*

Sara drew this pictogram to show the average number of hours animals sleep each day.

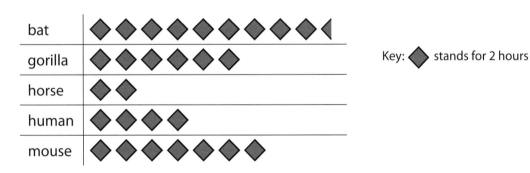

Key: ◆ stands for 2 hours

a Which animal sleeps for a shorter time each day than a human?

b A bat sleeps for longer each day than a mouse. How many hours longer?

c Now Dave draws another pictogram to show the same information.
Here is Dave's key:

Key: ⬤ stands for 3 hours

How many circles show the number of hours that a gorilla sleeps each day?

## Exercise 5B

**Venn and Carroll diagrams** are sorting diagrams. Every item must have a place to go.

These diagrams show in different ways whether six children have a brother or sister.

### Carroll diagram

|  | has brother | no brother |
|---|---|---|
| has sister | Josh | Anna Rob |
| no sister | Mia Ali | Ryan |

### Venn diagram

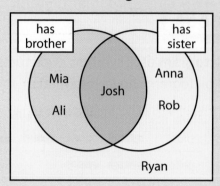

---

**1** *2004 level 3*

There are 30 pupils in class 9A. The table shows if they travel to school by train.

| Class 9A | travel by train | do not travel by train |
|---|---|---|
| **boys** | 4 | 12 |
| **girls** | 2 | 12 |

**a** Altogether, how many pupils in class 9A do not travel by train?

**b** The bar chart on the right shows how many pupils are in class 9B.

In class 9B, no boys travel by train.
Half of the girls travel by train.

Copy and complete the table below.

| Class 9B | travel by train | do not travel by train |
|---|---|---|
| **boys** | | |
| **girls** | | |

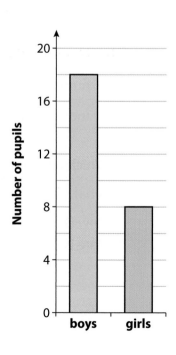

**2** *2003 KS2 level 3*

Copy this diagram.

|  | curved lines | no curved lines |
|---|---|---|
| **straight lines** |  |  |
| **no straight lines** |  |  |

Write each of these letters in the correct place on your diagram.

T     N     P     S

**3** *1998 KS2 level 3*

A group of six children sorted themselves into these sets.

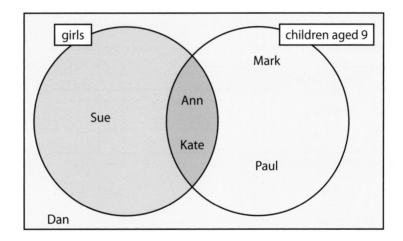

Copy and complete the table for the group.

| Boys | | Girls | |
|---|---|---|---|
| **Name** | **Age** | **Name** | **Age** |
| Mark | 9 |  | 9 |
|  | 8 | Ann |  |
|  | 9 |  | 8 |

Five children sorted themselves into these sets.

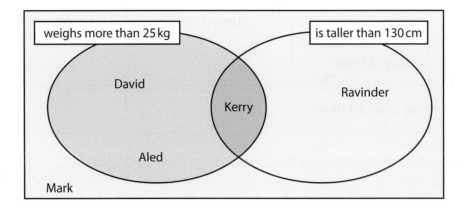

Copy and complete this diagram to show the same information.

|  | is taller than 130 cm | is not taller than 130 cm |
|---|---|---|
| **weighs more than 25 kg** |  |  |
| **does not weigh more than 25 kg** |  |  |

---

### ◉ Points to remember

⊙ In a Carroll diagram, all the data must go into one of the boxes.

⊙ In a Venn diagram, the data can go inside or outside the circles, depending on its properties.

⊙ A pictogram uses symbols or pictures to represent information:
  – a key is used to explain what each symbol represents.
  – a symbol may represent more than one item of data.
  – symbols must be the same size and lined up neatly.

# Answers to

# How well are you doing?

## N1.1 Properties of numbers

1   20, 580 and 400

2   11

3   a   40 + 30 = 70 and 60 + 10 = 70

    b   60 + 6 + 4 = 70

    c   100 − 30 = 70

4   940

5   26

6   49, 87 and 503

7   303, 313, 323

## G1.1 Properties of shapes

1   a   C     b   A and E     c   7

2

|  | Property of shape | |
| --- | --- | --- |
|  | is an octagon | has at least 1 right angle |
| shape A | ✗ | ✓ |
| shape B | ✓ | ✗ |
| shape C | ✗ | ✗ |
| shape D | ✓ | ✓ |

3   a   For example:

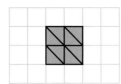

    b   For example:

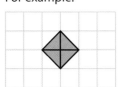

4   D4

## N1.2 Adding and subtracting

1   330

2   a   705 euros       b   1010 euros

3   a   46 + 27 = 73

    b   55 − 26 = 29

4   a   906

    b   159

5   36

6   10p, 5p, 2p, 1p, 1p or 5p, 5p, 5p, 2p, 2p

7   662

8   a   430       b   609       c   391 points

## A1.1 Patterns and sequences

1   a   1   4   7   10   **13**   **16**

       1   2   4   8   **16**   **32**

    b   Subtract 4.

       20   16   12   8   4   **0**   **−4**

2   No. 35 will not be shaded. Only even numbers are shaded.

3   Saturday.

4   a   75p

    b   £1.05

5   Choose from:

    1 × 24 = 24       or   24 × 1 = 24

    2 × 12 = 24       or   12 × 2 = 24

    3 × 8 = 24        or   8 × 3 = 24

    4 × 6 = 24        or   6 × 4 = 24

6   185

## G1.2 Angles and symmetry

1   a   i   No        ii   Yes

    b   i   Yes       ii   Yes

    c   i   Yes       ii   No

    d   i   No        ii   Yes

2   a

    b   Correct route with two norths and one east

    c   a different route with two norths and one east

3

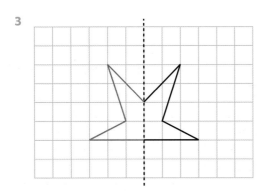

4    M and E

## N1.3 Multiplying and dividing

1    36, 28, 24, 22, 21
2    a    20 points
     b    2 hoops on the 8 points peg
          1 hoop on the 6 points peg
3    a    168                    b    26
4    a    $9 \times 13 = 117$    b    $15 \times 6 = 90$
     c    $108 \div 9 = 12$      d    $16 \times 8 = 128$
5    a    1000         b    483        c    56
6    £272.35

## S1.1 Graphs and charts 1

1    a    10         b    14         c    3
2    a    5          b    2
3    7

## N1.4 Mental calculations

1    a    add 6                  b    subtract 8
2    a    83                     b    37
     c    62
3    a    24
     b    any two numbers that sum to 34
4    a    10                     b    18
     c    20                     d    30
5    103

## G1.3 Measures 1

1    A and E, B and F, C and D
2    45 minutes
3    a    30 minutes             b    9:25
4    a    C 2 m        b    B 14 cm        c    D 64 km
5    Accurately drawn 9 cm line
6    The sunflower is 3 m 60 cm tall.
7    7.5 cm

## N1.5 Fractions

1    a    Half                   b    More than half
     c    Half
2    a    Shape E
     b    No, $\frac{1}{2}$ of 20 and $\frac{1}{4}$ of 40 both equal 10.
3    $\frac{1}{2}$
4    $\frac{1}{2}$ and $\frac{5}{10}$
5    20 cherries
6    $\frac{2}{5}$
7    a    3          b    $\frac{1}{2}$        c    15

## S1.2 Graphs and charts 2

1
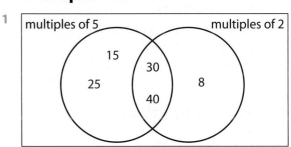

2    a    101
     b    247
3    a    7                      b    15
4    8
5    a    autumn and winter
     b    15

## N1.6 Money and decimals

1    a    5.7                    b    6.2
2    a    Toast and tea: cost £1.55
     b    Pizza and juice: £2.40
3    a    Any number between 1000 and 1100,
          e.g. 1065
     b    Any decimal between 0 and 1, e.g. 0.5
4    $538 + 46 = 584$
5    £26.89
6    a    5 tickets    b    6 tickets    c    £22

## G1.4 Measures 2

1    a    6:45 am                b    7:15 pm
2    a    09:15; 45 minutes
     b    09:30
     c    £11
3    3 kg

**4** **a** 3 kg **b** 300 ml

**5** 300 ml

## N1.7 Number and measures

**1** **a** bird
 **b** diver
 **c** fish

**2** **a** 5°C
 **b** −9°C, −3°C, 0°C, 6°C

**3** 125 ml

**4** **a** NO. There are 100 cm in one metre.
 **b** There are 10 mm in one centimetre.

**5** **a** A is −3 and B is 13.
 The numbers go up in steps of 4.
 **b** C is 7.9, D is 8.0 and E is 8.1.
 The numbers go up in steps of 0.1.

## G1.5 More properties of shapes

**1** **a** E, D
 **b** equal sides, lines of symmetry

**2** octagon

**3** **a** *d*
 **b** right angle or 90°

**4** **a** (5, 2)
 **b** (2, 1)

## N1.8 Multiplying and dividing 2

**1** **a** 7 **b** 24

**2** **a** 24 × 13 = **312**
 **b** 15 × **20** = 300
 **c** 288 ÷ 24 = **12**
 **d** **22 × 12** = 264 or **12 × 22** = 264

**3** **a** 168 **b** 26

**4** 364.8 kilometres

**5** 34

**6** **a** 140 plants **b** 12 trays

## S1.3 Graphs and charts 3

**1**

| football | ○ | ○ | ○ | ○ |
|---|---|---|---|---|
| tennis | ○ | ○ | | |
| cricket | ○ | ○ | ○ | |

**2** **a** 4
 **b**

| | Number of boys | Number of girls |
|---|---|---|
| **Right-handed** | 11 | 9 |
| **Left-handed** | 2 | 3 |

**3** Dr Rawley

**4**

| | girls | not girls |
|---|---|---|
| **aged 9** | Amy Kelly | Max Peter |
| **not aged 9** | Sarah | David |

## G1.6 Measures 3

**1** **a** 6 cups **b** 4 cups

**2** **a** A 6 B 18
 **b** A 30 B 90
 **c** A 33 B 39
 **d** A 65 B 95

**3** 20 cm, 0.5 m, 130 cm, 1.4 m

**4** 70 minutes

**5** A and D

**6** **a** Tuesday
 **b** 30th September
 **c** 122 days

## N1.9 Solving number problems

**1** **a** For example, when you multiply 2 by 3 you get 6, which is an even number.
 **b** For example, 8 is an even number. When you divide it by 2 you get 4, which is even, not odd.

**2** No. The even numbers are shaded. 35 is an odd number, so it will not be shaded.

**3** 71p, 72p, 75p

**4** **a** 853 **b** 538

**5** **a** 3 games.
 **b** Ed
 **c** The cross shows you cannot play a game against yourself.

**6** 25, 27, 52, 57, 72, 75

# Index